NEW PARK SCHOO'

MATHS FRAMEWORKING

Complete support for Mathematics at KS3

YEAR 8

TEACHER'S PACK 1

KEVIN EVANS   KEITH GORDON   TREVOR SENIOR   BRIAN SPEED

Contents

© HarperCollins*Publishers* Ltd 2003

Introduction

This is the lower-level teaching text for Year 8. It accompanies *Maths Frameworking* Year 8 Pupil Book 1. Students who are working at a level above this are catered for by Pupil Book 2 and Teacher's Pack 2. Those working at the highest level are catered for by Pupil Book 3 and Teacher's Pack 3. The majority of topics and their sequence are the same across all three books but are handled at different levels, allowing for sensitive differentiation in mixed-ability classes.

Maths Frameworking has been based totally on the finalised National Numeracy Strategy document. The detailed lesson plans deliver core material from the *Framework for Teaching Mathematics: Year 8*. We have reduced the teaching time from the 105 hours recommended in the NNS to around 90 one-hour lessons. This should enable teachers some flexibility to include tests, extended activities and revision classes in their teaching programme, and allows for the normal events that disrupt teaching time.

Each lesson plan follows the same format with the following features:

- **Framework objectives** to identify the key learning outcomes from the Framework
- Engaging **Oral and mental starter** activities to involve the whole class
- **Main lesson activities** to help you lead students into exercise questions
- **Plenary** guidance to round off the NNS three-part lesson
- **Key words** which highlight when to introduce Framework Vocabulary terms
- Extra **Homework questions** to consolidate and extend learning
- **Answers** for all pupil book, homework and SATs-style questions

  PLUS

  The **free CD-ROM** that comes with each teacher pack allows you to customise your lessons to produce individualised teaching programmes for students and to reproduce diagrams for use on overhead projectors or electronic whiteboards. Full details of how to use this resource are given on pages x–xii.

Chapter numbers and titles in Maths Frameworking follow the NNS exactly. For further help in mapping lessons and producing your scheme of work, please consult the contents pages and the matching charts that follow.

The Oral and mental starters are designed to work with minimal specialised equipment – a blackboard and a piece of chalk would suffice – but resources such as OHPs, A3-sized target boards, counting sticks, number squares, student white boards and number fans make the activities easier to present and more accessible to students. A selection of inexpensive or free numeracy resources are available from Collins. See the accompanying website www.mathsframeworking.com for details.

The authors recognise that ICT provision in schools is varied and we have tried not to commit teachers to an activity that they could not carry out. However, suggestions for activities using ICT are included in the table below. Some lessons also address cross-curricular issues such as Literacy.

Lesson number and title		ICT activity	Pupil Book page no.
1.2	HCF and LCM	Extension Work ◆ Spreadsheet investigation of Triangle and Square numbers	p. 6
1.5	Sequences 1	Extension Work ◆ Internet and spreadsheet investigation of Fibonacci sequence	p. 12
2.5	Constructions	Extension Work ◆ Using LOGO to draw triangles	p. 27
3.2	Probability scales	Extension Work ◆ Designing a spreadsheet to calculate probabilities	p. 34
5.4	Using algebra and shapes	Extension Work ◆ Using a spreadsheet to verify algebraic statements	p. 59
9.2	Combinations of transformations	Extension Work ◆ Exploring combined transformations of shapes using LOGO	p. 108
13.6	Change of subject	Extension Work ◆ Using a spreadsheet to add up a large list of numbers	p. 160
14.4	Proportion	Extension Work ◆ Designing a spreadsheet to calculate percentage increase	p. 168
15.4	To construct a triangle given three sides	Extension Work ◆ Using LOGO to draw triangles	p. 181
15.5	Loci	Extension Work ◆ Using LOGO to generate loci	p. 183
16.6	Experimental and theoretical probability	Extension Work ◆ Simulating a simple experiment using a spreadsheet or other software	p. 200

National Test SAT-style questions are provided at the end of each chapter along with levelling guides to help students assess their own grasp of key objectives. Answers are provided in the last lesson plan of each chapter.

Extra practice exercises are also available in the accompanying Year 8 Practice Book 1. This is an ideal resource for catch-up classes or for use as a homework book.

A start of year SAT-style levelling test, SAT-style half-termly tests and end of chapter tests are available in the Year 8 Assessment Test Pack.

The NNS is intended to improve standards. This can only be done by the good work of teachers in the classroom. The authors appreciate the good work teachers do and hope that *Maths Frameworking* proves a suitable resource to help them.

Kevin Evans, Keith Gordon, Trevor Senior and Brian Speed

Framework Objectives Matching Chart

This chart matches the National Strategy Framework Objectives to specific lesson plans contained in this Teacher Pack. The objectives are taken from the *Year 8 Teaching Programme* of the DfES's completed *National Strategy Framework for Teaching Mathematics*, published April 2001. The page references given with each objective correspond to the Supplement of Examples for Years 7, 8 and 9 in Section 4 of that document.

Where a lesson plan only partially addresses an objective, this is indicated by a ★.

Objectives	Chapter title	Lesson number and title
Using and applying mathematics to solve problems **Applying mathematics and solving problems**		
• Solve more demanding problems and investigate in a range of contexts: number, algebra, shape, space and measures, and handling data; compare and evaluate solutions. pp. 2–25	Number and Algebra 1 Solving Problems Shape, Space and Measures 1	1.7 Solving problems 14.1 Number and measures 2.4 The geometric properties of quadrilaterals
• Identify the necessary information to solve a problem; represent problems and interpret solutions in algebraic, geometric or graphical form, using correct notation and appropriate diagrams. pp. 26–7	Solving Problems	14.2 Using words and diagrams to solve problems ★
• Solve more complex problems by breaking them into smaller steps or tasks, choosing and using efficient techniques for calculation, algebraic manipulation and graphical representation, and resources, including ICT. pp. 28–9	Number and Algebra 1 Solving Problems	1.7 Solving problems ★ 14.2 Using words and diagrams to solve problems ★
• Use logical argument to establish the truth of a statement; give solutions to an appropriate degree of accuracy in the context of the problem. pp. 30–1	Solving Problems	14.3 Logical solutions and best value
• Suggest extensions to problems, conjecture and generalise; identify exceptional cases or counter-examples. pp. 32–5	Solving Problems	14.3 Logical solutions and best value ★
Numbers and the number system **Place value, ordering and rounding**		
• Read and write positive integer powers of 10; multiply and divide integers and decimals by 0.1, 0.01. pp. 36–9	Number 3	8.1 Rounding
• Order decimals. pp. 40–1		
• Round positive numbers to any given power of 10; round decimals to the nearest whole number or to one or two decimal places. pp. 42–5	Number 3	8.2 Large numbers
Integers, powers and roots		
• Add, subtract, multiply and divide integers. pp. 48–51	Number and Algebra 1	1.1 Multiplying and dividing negative numbers
• Recognise and use multiples, factors (divisors), common factor, highest common factor, lowest common multiple and primes; find the prime factor decomposition of a number (e.g. $8000 = 2^6 \times 5^3$). pp. 52–5	Number and Algebra 1	1.2 HCF and LCM 1.4 Prime factors
• Use squares, positive and negative square roots, cubes and cube roots, and index notation for small positive integer powers. pp. 56–9	Number and Algebra 1	1.3 Powers and roots
Fractions, decimals, percentages, ratio and proportion		
• Know that a recurring decimal is a fraction; use division to convert a fraction to a decimal; order fractions by writing them with a common denominator or by converting them to decimals. pp. 60–5	Number 2	4.1 Fractions and decimals
• Add and subtract fractions by writing them with a common denominator; calculate fractions of quantities (fraction answers); multiply and divide an integer by a fraction. pp. 66–9	Number 2	4.2 Adding and subtracting fractions
• Interpret percentage as the operator 'so many hundredths of' and express one given number as a percentage of another; use the equivalence of fractions, decimals and percentages to compare proportions; calculate percentages and find the outcome of a given percentage increase or decrease. pp. 70–7	Number 2	4.3 Percentages ★ 4.4 Percentage increase and decrease ★

Objectives	Chapter title	Lesson number and title
• Consolidate understanding of the relationship between ratio and proportion; reduce a ratio to its simplest form, including a ratio expressed in different units, recognising links with fraction notation; divide a quantity into two or more parts in a given ratio; use the unitary method to solve simple word problems involving ratio and direct proportion. pp. 78–81	Shape, Space and Measures 3 Solving Problems	9.5 Shape and ratio ★ 14.4 Proportion ★ 14.5 Ratio ★

Calculations
Number operations and the relationships between them

Objectives	Chapter title	Lesson number and title
• Understand addition and subtraction of fractions and integers, and multiplication and division of integers; use the laws of arithmetic and inverse operations. pp. 82–5	Number 4	12.1 Fractions ★ 12.2 Adding and subtracting fractions ★
• Use the order of operations, including brackets, with more complex calculations. pp. 86–7	Number 4	12.3 BODMAS

Mental methods and rapid recall of number facts

Objectives	Chapter title	Lesson number and title
• Recall known facts, including fraction to decimal conversions; use known facts to derive unknown facts, including products involving numbers such as 0.7 and 6, and 0.03 and 8. pp. 88–91	Number 2	4.5 Real-life problems *Starter activities throughout book*
• Consolidate and extend mental methods of calculation, working with decimals, fractions and percentages, squares and square roots, cubes and cube roots; solve word problems mentally. pp. 92–101	Number 3	*Starter activities throughout book*
• Make and justify estimates and approximations of calculations. pp. 102–3	Number 3	8.3 Estimations

Written methods

Objectives	Chapter title	Lesson number and title
• Consolidate standard column procedures for addition and subtraction of integers and decimals with up to two places. pp. 104–5	Number 3	8.4 Adding and subtracting decimals
• Use standard column procedures for multiplication and division of integers and decimals, including by decimals such as 0.6 or 0.06; understand where to position the decimal point by considering equivalent calculations. pp. 104–7	Number 3 Number 4	8.6 Long multiplication and long division 12.4 Multiplying decimals 12.5 Dividing decimals

Calculator methods

Objectives	Chapter title	Lesson number and title
• Carry out more difficult calculations effectively and efficiently using the function keys for sign change, powers, roots and fractions; use brackets and the memory. pp. 108–9	Number 3	8.5 Efficient calculations
• Enter numbers and interpret the display in different contexts (negative numbers, fractions, decimals, percentages, money, metric measures, time). pp. 108–9	Number 3	8.5 Efficient calculations

Checking results

Objectives	Chapter title	Lesson number and title
• Check a result by considering whether it is of the right order of magnitude and by working the problem backwards. pp. 110–11	Number 3	8.3 Estimations 8.5 Efficient calculations

Algebra
Equations, formulae and identities

Objectives	Chapter title	Lesson number and title
• Begin to distinguish the different roles played by letter symbols in equations, formulae and functions; know the meanings of the words formula and function. pp. 112–3	Algebra 2	5.1 Algebraic shorthand 5.4 Using algebra with shapes
• Know that algebraic operations follow the same conventions and order as arithmetic operations; use index notation for small positive integer powers. pp. 114–5	Algebra 2	5.1 Algebraic shorthand 5.2 Two rules of algebra
• Simplify or transform linear expressions by collecting like terms; multiply a single term over a bracket. pp. 116–9	Algebra 2 Algebra 5	5.2 Two rules of algebra 5.3 Like terms and simplification 5.5 Expanding brackets 13.1 Expanding brackets 13.6 Change of subject
• Construct and solve linear equations with integer coefficients (unknown on either or both sides, without and with brackets) using appropriate methods (e.g. inverse operations, transforming both sides in same way). pp. 122–5	Algebra 4 Algebra 5	10.1 Puzzle mappings ★ 10.2 Puzzle mappings involving more than one operation ★ 10.3 Solving equations ★ 13.2 Solving equations ★ 13.3 Constructing equations to solve ★
• Begin to use graphs and set up equations to solve simple problems involving direct proportion. pp. 136–7		

Objectives	Chapter title	Lesson number and title
• Use formulae from mathematics and other subjects; substitute integers into simple formulae, including examples that lead to an equation to solve, and positive integers into expressions involving small powers (e.g. $3x^2 + 4$ or $2x^3$); derive simple formulae. pp. 138–43	Algebra 4	10.4 Substituting into expressions ★ 10.5 Substituting into formulae ★ 10.6 Creating your own expressions and formulae ★
Sequences, functions and graphs		
• Generate and describe simple integer sequences. pp. 144–7	Number and Algebra 1	1.5 Sequences 1
• Generate terms of a linear sequence using term-to-term and position-to-term definitions of the sequence, on paper and using a spreadsheet or graphical calculator. pp. 148–51	Number and Algebra 1	1.5 Sequences 1 1.6 Sequences 2
• Begin to use linear expressions to describe the nth term of an arithmetic sequence, justifying its form by referring to the activity or practical context from which it was generated. pp. 154–7	Number and Algebra 1	1.6 Sequences 2
• Express simple functions in symbols; represent mappings expressed algebraically. pp. 160–3	Algebra 3	7.1 Linear functions ★ 7.2 Finding a function from its inputs and outputs ★
• Generate points in all four quadrants and plot the graphs of linear functions, where y is given explicitly in terms of x, on paper and using ICT; recognise that equations of the form $y = mx + c$ correspond to straight-line graphs. pp. 164–7	Algebra 3 Algebra 5	7.3 Graphs from functions ★ 7.4 Rules with coordinates ★ 13.4 Lines and equations ★
• Construct linear functions arising from real-life problems and plot their corresponding graphs; discuss and interpret graphs arising from real situations. pp. 172–7	Algebra 3 Algebra 5	7.5 Distance–time graphs ★ 13.5 Real-life graphs ★
Shape, space and measures **Geometrical reasoning: lines, angles and shapes**		
• Identify alternate angles and corresponding angles; understand a proof that: – the sum of the angles of a triangle is 180° and of a quadrilateral is 360°; – the exterior angle of a triangle is equal to the sum of the two interior opposite angles. pp. 178–83	Shape, Space and Measures 1	2.3 Calculating angles ★
• Solve geometrical problems using side and angle properties of equilateral, isosceles and right-angled triangles and special quadrilaterals, explaining reasoning with diagrams and text; classify quadrilaterals by their geometric properties. pp. 184–9	Shape, Space and Measures 1	2.4 The geometric properties of quadrilaterals
• Know that if two 2-D shapes are congruent, corresponding sides and angles are equal. pp. 190–1	Shape, Space and Measures 3	9.1 Congruent shapes
• Know and use geometric properties of cuboids and shapes made from cuboids; begin to use plans and elevations. pp. 198–201	Shape, Space and Measures 4	15.1 Plans and elevations ★
Transformations		
• Transform 2-D shapes by simple combinations of rotations, reflections and translations, on paper and using ICT; identify all the symmetries of 2-D shapes. pp. 202–11	Shape, Space and Measures 3	9.2 Combinations of transformations ★ 9.4 Reflections in two mirror lines ★
• Understand and use the language and notation associated with enlargement; enlarge 2-D shapes, given a centre of enlargement and a positive whole-number scale factor; explore enlargement using ICT. pp. 212–15		
• Make simple scale drawings. pp. 216–7	Shape, Space and Measures 4	15.3 Scale drawings
Coordinates		
• Given the coordinates of points A and B, find the mid-point of the line segment AB. pp. 218–9		
Construction and loci		
• Use straight edge and compasses to construct: – the mid-point and perpendicular bisector of a line segment; – the bisector of an angle; – perpendicular from a point to a line; – perpendicular from a point on a line; – a triangle, given three sides (SSS); – use ICT to explore these constructions. pp. 220–3	Shape, Space and Measures 4	15.5 To construct a triangle given three sides ★
• Find simple loci, both by reasoning and by using ICT, to produce shapes and paths, e.g. an equilateral triangle. pp. 224–7	Shape, Space and Measures 4	15.6 Loci

Objectives	Chapter title	Lesson number and title
Measures and mensuration		
• Use units of measurement to estimate, calculate and solve problems in everyday contexts involving length, area, volume, capacity, mass, time, angle and bearings; know rough metric equivalents of imperial measures in daily use (feet, miles, pounds, pints, gallons). pp. 228–31	Shape, Space and Measures 2 Shape, Space and Measures 4	6.1 Perimeter and area of rectangles 6.3 Reading scales 6.5 Converting one metric unit into another 15.6 Bearings
• Use bearings to specify direction. pp. 232–3	Shape, Space and Measures 4	15.7 Bearings
• Deduce and use formulae for the area of a triangle, parallelogram and trapezium; calculate areas of compound shapes made from rectangles and triangles. pp. 234–7	Shape, Space and Measures 2	6.2 The perimeter and area of compound shapes ★
• Know and use the formula for the volume of a cuboid; calculate volumes and surface areas of cuboids and shapes made from cuboids. pp. 238–41	Shape, Space and Measures 2 Shape, Space and Measures 4	6.4 Surface area of cubes and cuboids ★ 15.8 A cube investigation ★
Handling data **Specifying a problem, planning and collecting data**		
• Discuss a problem that can be addressed by statistical methods and identify related questions to explore. pp. 248–9	Handling Data 2	11.1 Statistical surveys 11.5 Analysing data
• Decide which data to collect to answer a question, and the degree of accuracy needed; identify possible sources. pp. 250–1	Handling Data 2	11.1 Statistical surveys 11.5 Analysing data
• Plan how to collect the data, including sample size; construct frequency tables with given equal class intervals for sets of continuous data; design and use two-way tables for discrete data. pp. 252–5	Handling Data 2 Handling Data 3	11.1 Statistical surveys 11.5 Analysing data 16.1 Frequency tables ★
• Collect data using a suitable method, such as observation, controlled experiment, including data logging using ICT, or questionnaire. pp. 254–5	Handling Data 2	11.1 Statistical surveys 11.5 Analysing data
Processing and representing data, using ICT as appropriate		
• Calculate statistics, including with a calculator; recognise when it is appropriate to use the range, mean, median and mode and, for grouped data, the modal class; calculate a mean using an assumed mean; construct and use stem-and-leaf diagrams. pp. 256–61	Handling Data 2 Handling Data 3	11.2 Stem-and-leaf diagrams 16.2 The median ★ 16.5 Which average to use?
• Construct, on paper and using ICT: – pie charts for categorical data; – bar charts and frequency diagrams for discrete and continuous data; – simple line graphs for time series; – simple scatter graphs; Identify which are most useful in the context of the problem. pp. 262–7	Handling Data 2 Handling Data 3	11.3 Pie charts 11.4 Scatter graphs 16.3 Drawing frequency diagrams ★
Interpreting and discussing results		
• Interpret tables, graphs and diagrams for both discrete and continuous data, and draw inferences that relate to the problem being discussed; relate summarised data to the questions being explored. pp. 268–71		
• Compare two distributions using the range and one or more of the mode, median and mean. pp. 272–3	Handling Data 3	16.4 Comparing data
• Communicate orally and on paper the results of a statistical enquiry and the methods used, using ICT as appropriate; justify the choice of what is presented. pp. 272–3	Handling Data 2 Handling Data 3	11.1 Statistical surveys 11.5 Analysing data 16.6 Experimental and theoretical probability
Probability		
• Use the vocabulary of probability when interpreting the results of an experiment; appreciate that random processes are unpredictable. pp. 276–7	Handling Data 1	3.1 Probability
• Know that if the probability of an event occurring is p, then the probability of it not occurring is $1 - p$; find and record all possible mutually exclusive outcomes for single events and two successive events in a systematic way, using diagrams and tables. pp. 278–81	Handling Data 1	3.2 Probability scales ★
• Estimate probabilities from experimental data; understand that: – if an experiment is repeated there may be, and usually will be, different outcomes; – increasing the number of times an experiment is repeated generally leads to better estimates of probability. pp. 282–3	Handling Data 1	3.3 Collecting data ★ 3.5 Experimental probability
• Compare experimental and theoretical probabilities in different contexts. pp. 284–5	Handling Data 1 Handling Data 3	3.4 Events ★ 16.6 Experimental and theoretical probability

Maths Frameworking
Year 8 Teacher Pack 1 CD-ROM

This free **Maths Frameworking Teacher Pack CD-ROM** provides all the pages of this pack in PDF format. These can be read by Adobe Acrobat Reader. If your computer does not already have the Acrobat Reader software it can be installed directly from the CD-ROM (please refer to the installation instructions below).

If your computer already has Acrobat Reader installed, follow these steps to view the **Maths Frameworking Teacher Pack CD-ROM**:

Macintosh

- Insert the Maths Frameworking Teacher Pack CD-ROM into your CD-ROM drive.
- Double-click the Maths Frameworking icon.

PC

For Windows:
- Click the 'Start' button and select 'Run'.
- Type 'D:\MF.pdf'. If you are not using the D drive as your CD-ROM drive, replace D with the appropriate letter.
- Click 'OK'.

Using the Maths Frameworking Teacher Pack CD-ROM

These pages contains brief guidance to help you to move around the CD, to enlarge and print pages and to adapt any of the activities to suit your own requirements.

For further, extensive help in using Acrobat Reader with the CD-ROM, select 'Reader Online Guide' from the 'Help' menu within Acrobat Reader.

Navigating the CD-ROM

Use the black, triangular direction buttons at the top of the screen to move forwards or backwards between pages of text.

You can also navigate your way around by clicking on the 'bookmarks' to each lesson, that appear on the left hand side of the screen. If a plus or minus sign appears to the left of a bookmark then you can click on this to show or hide subordinate bookmarks.

Printing the PDF pages

Select the print options you want by using 'Page Setup' in the 'File' menu. When you are ready to print, select 'Print' from the 'File' menu and specify the pages that you wish to print.

Adapting the text

You can select text or a graphic from the lesson plans and copy it to the Clipboard. Once the selected text or graphic is on the Clipboard you can switch to another application, such as a word processor or graphics package, and paste it into a new or existing document. (**Note**: *If a font copied from a PDF document is not available on the system displaying the copied text, the font cannot be preserved. Helvetica is substituted.*)

To select text and copy it to the Clipboard:

1 From the Tool Bar choose the Text Select icon.

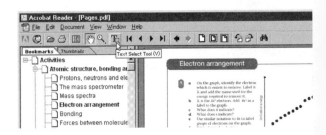

To select a line (or lines) of text, select the first letter of the sentence or phrase and drag to the last letter. To select a vertical section of text without selecting text on either side, hold down the Ctrl (Windows and UNIX) or Option (Mac OS) key as you drag across the document. To select all the text on the page, choose Edit > Select All.

2 From the 'Edit' menu select 'Copy' to copy the selected text to the Clipboard. You can then view what you have selected by choosing 'Show Clipboard' from the 'Window' menu. (*Note: In Windows 95, the Clipboard viewer is not installed by default; therefore, you cannot use the Show Clipboard command until you install it. Install the Clipboard viewer by choosing Start > Settings > Control Panel > Add/ Remove Programs and clicking the Windows Setup tab. Double-click Accessories, check Clipboard viewer, and click 'OK'.*)

To select and copy graphics to the Clipboard:

1 Choose the Graphics Select tool by holding down the mouse button on the Text Select icon and dragging to the Graphics Select tool. Or press Shift-V as necessary to cycle through the group of tools. The cursor changes to a cross-hair icon.

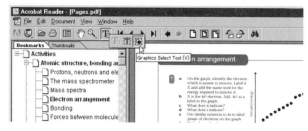

2 Drag a rectangle around the graphic you want to copy. To deselect the graphic and start over, click anywhere outside the selected graphic.
3 From the 'Edit' menu select 'Copy' to copy the selected graphic to the Clipboard. The graphic is copied in a WMF format for Windows, and a PICT for Macintosh.
(*Notes: Copied graphics may include text, but text copied with this tool will not be editable by a word processor. Use the Text Select tool for any text you wish to be able to edit.*
In case of copied graphics being of low resolution, try zooming in, using the magnifying glass tool, to make the desired section appear as large as possible before selecting and copying it.)

Adobe Acrobat Reader 5 software
Installation

Macintosh

● Insert the CD-ROM into your CD-ROM drive.
● Double-click the 'Install Acrobat Reader 5' icon that appears in the window.

PC

For Windows:
● Click the 'Start' button and select 'Run'.
● Type 'D:\acroread\rp500enu.exe'. If you are not using the D drive as your CD-ROM drive, replace D with the appropriate letter.
● Click 'OK'.
Note that this is Adobe Acrobat 5 installer, but all files on this CD-ROM are compatible with Adobe Acrobat 4. Adobe Acrobat 5 will not run on Windows 3.1 or non-Power Macintoshes.

System Requirements

Macintosh

● PowerPC processor
● Mac OS software version 8.6, 9.0.4, 9.1, or Mac OS X
● 32 MB of RAM (with virtual memory on) (64 MB recommended)
● 150 MB of available hard-disk space

PC

● Intel Pentium processor
● Microsoft Windows 95 OSR 2.0, Windows 98, Windows Millennium, Windows NT 4.0 with Service Pack 5 or 6, Windows 2000, or Windows XP
● 32 MB of RAM (64 MB recommended)
● 150 MB of available hard-disk space

Help

When using Acrobat Reader, select 'Reader Online Guide' from the Help menu.

Attributions

Adobe and Acrobat are trademarks of Adobe Systems Incorporated.

Windows is a registered trademark and Windows NT is a trademark of Microsoft in the U.S. and other countries. Pentium is a registered trademark of Intel Corporation.

Macintosh and Power Macintosh are registered trademarks of Apple Computer, Inc.

Restrictions on use

Published by HarperCollins*Publishers* Ltd

77–85 Fulham Palace Road, London W6 8JB

© HarperCollins*Publishers* Ltd 2003

First published 2003

Maths Frameworking Year 8
Lesson Plans

For use with Maths Frameworking Year 8 Pupil Book 1

CHAPTER 1

Number and Algebra 1

LESSON 1.1

Framework objectives – Multiplying and dividing negative numbers
Add, subtract, multiply and divide integers.

Oral and mental starter

- Use a number line drawn on the board or a counting stick with 10 segments marked on it. State that the right end (as the students look at it) is 0.

```
▭▬▭▬▭▬▭▬▭▬
                                    0
```

- Point out that as the students look at the line, the values to the left of zero are negative.
- Give a value to each segment, say –1, and as a group or with an individual count down the line in steps of –1 from zero. The students can have the positions pointed out to them on the line until the end is reached, then continue without prompts.
- Repeat with other values for the segments, such as –2, –3, –4.
- Now give a value to each segment, say –6. Then point at a position on the line, say the fourth division, and ask what value it represents.
- Repeat with other values for each segment and different positions on the line.

Main lesson activity

- Draw a number line on the board and mark it from –10 to +10.
- First, recall the rules for dealing with directed number problems using the number line. Give some examples, such as $3 - 7 (= -4)$, $-2 - 3 (= -5)$, $-5 + 8 (= 3)$.
- Now ask the students to complete the following patterns.

  a $5 + {+1} = 6$ **b** $-3 - {+1} = -4$
  $ 5 + 0 = 5$ $-3 - 0 = -3$
  $ 5 + {-1} = 4$ $-3 - {-1} = -2$
  $ 5 + {-2} = \ldots$ $-3 - {-2} = \ldots$
  $ 5 + \ldots = \ldots$ $-3 - \ldots = \ldots$
  $ 5 + \ldots = \ldots$ $-3 - \ldots = \ldots$

- Establish that when we add a positive number, it is the same as addition. The class may be given the rules $+ + = +$, $+ - = -$, $- + = -$, $- - = +$, but note that these can lead to confusion with problems such as $-3 - 4$.
- Demonstrate how these work with problems such as $3 - -4 = 3 + 4 = 7$.
- If necessary, they can do Questions 1 to 3 in Exercise 1A from Pupil Book 1.
- Now ask for the answer to $-2 + -2 + -2 + -2 + -2 (= -10)$. Ask whether there is another way to write this: that is, 5×-2. (Recall that multiplication is repeated addition.)
- Repeat with other examples, such as $- -4 - -4 - -4 = -3 \times -4 (= +12)$.
- Ask the class whether they can see a quick way to work out products such as $-2 \times +3$, -5×-4, $+7 \times +3$.
- They should come up with the rule that it is the product of the numbers combined with the rules for combining signs.
- The $- \times - = +$ can cause problems. Ask the class to complete this pattern:
  $$+2 \times -3 = -6$$
  $$+1 \times -3 = -3$$
  $$0 \times \ldots = \ldots$$
  $$-1 \times \ldots = \ldots \text{ , and so on.}$$

- This can then be linked to division. For example: $-3 \times +6 = -18$, so $-18 \div -3 = +6$; $+5 \times -3 = -15$, so $-15 \div +5 = -3$.
- Once again, ask the students to explain a quick way of doing these. As for multiplication, the numbers are divided normally and the sign of the answer is determined by the combination of signs in the original problem.

- **The class can now do Exercise 1A from Pupil Book 1.**

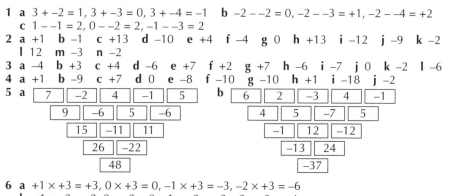

Exercise 1A Answers

1 a $3 + -2 = 1$, $3 + -3 = 0$, $3 + -4 = -1$ **b** $-2 - -2 = 0$, $-2 - -3 = +1$, $-2 - -4 = +2$
 c $1 - -1 = 2$, $0 - -2 = 2$, $-1 - -3 = 2$
2 a +1 **b** –1 **c** +13 **d** –10 **e** +4 **f** –4 **g** 0 **h** +13 **i** –12 **j** –9 **k** –2
 l 12 **m** –3 **n** –2
3 a –4 **b** +3 **c** +4 **d** –6 **e** +7 **f** +2 **g** +7 **h** –6 **i** –7 **j** 0 **k** –2 **l** –6
4 a +1 **b** –9 **c** +7 **d** 0 **e** –8 **f** –10 **g** –10 **h** +1 **i** –18 **j** –2
5 a

7	–2	4	–1	5

9	–6	5	–6

15	–11	11

26	–22

48

b

6	2	–3	4	–1

4	5	–7	5

–1	12	–12

–13	24

–37

6 a $+1 \times +3 = +3$, $0 \times +3 = 0$, $-1 \times +3 = -3$, $-2 \times +3 = -6$
 b $+1 \times -2 = -2$, $0 \times -2 = 0$, $-1 \times -2 = +2$, $-2 \times -2 = +4$
 c $-1 \times +1 = -1$, $0 \times +1 = 0$, $+1 \times +1 = +1$, $+2 \times +1 = +2$, $+ 3 \times +1 = + 3$
7 a –6 **b** –12 **c** –10 **d** +18 **e** –24 **f** –20 **g** +12 **h** +6 **i** –14 **j** +16
 k –60 **l** +32 **m** +30 **n** –18 **o** +16
8 a –4 **b** –6 **c** –3 **d** +2 **e** –4 **f** –8 **g** +8 **h** +6 **i** –3.5 **j** +2 **k** –6
 l +2 **m** +7.5 **n** –9 **o** +4
9 a –6 **b** +4 **c** –3 **d** 75 **e** +24 **f** +8 **g** –2 **h** +6 **i** –6

Extension Answers

9, –14, 11; 4, 2, 0; –7, 18, –5; –6, –1, –8; –7, –5, –3; –2, –9, –4

Plenary

- Ask some mental questions. For example:
 'What is: $6 - 9$; $-5 - + 3$; $-4 - 3$; $-2 \times +7$; $-32 \div -8$?'
- Encourage the students to 'say the problem to themselves'. For example, for $+7 - -2$, say: 'Plus seven minus minus two.'
- Make sure that nobody is left confused by 'two negatives make a positive'. For example, several students will state that '$-6 - 7 = +13$'.

Key Words

- positive
- negative
- multiply
- divide
- inverse operation

Homework

1 Work out the answer to each of these.

 a $-4 + 5 - 7$ **b** $+7 - 2 - 8$

 c $-2 - -3 + -5$ **d** $-4 - -5 - +6$

 e $-2 + 7 + 2$ **f** $- +6 + -8 - -6$

2 Find each missing number.

 a $+6 - \square = -2$ **b** $\square - -3 = -6$

 c $+8 + \square = 2$ **d** $\square + \square = 0$

3 Work out the answer to each of these.

 a 5×-4 **b** -2×4 **c** -6×3

 d -3×-3 **e** -2×9 **f** $15 \div -5$

 g $-24 \div 3$ **h** $-8 \div 2$ **i** $-9 \div -3$

 j $-40 \div 5$

4 Find each missing number.

 a $5 \times -3 = \square$ **b** $-2 \times \square = -10$
 c $3 \times \square = -12$

Answers
1 a –6 **b** –3 **c** –4 **d** –5 **e** +7 **f** –8
2 a +8 **b** –9 **c** –6 **d** Any pair ±
3 a –20 **b** –8 **c** –18 **d** 9 **e** –18 **f** –3
 g –8 **h** –4 **i** 3 **j** –8
4 a –15 **b** 5 **c** –4

Framework objectives – HCF and LCM
Recognise and use multiples, factors (divisors), common factor, highest common factor, lowest common multiple and primes.

Oral and mental starter

- The students should use a number fan or a white board on which to write their answers.
- They should not hold up these until requested to avoid weaker students copying the answers.
- Ask for an example of an even number; a multiple of 6; a factor of 12; a prime number; a square number; a number that is a multiple of both 3 and 4; a triangle number; etc.
- Go around the class for each example, checking each student's answer.
- If necessary, discuss and define what was required.
- Particularly emphasise factors and multiples, as these will be used in the main lesson activity.

Main lesson activity

- Keeping their fans or cards, ask the students if they wrote down a number that is a multiple of both 3 and 4 (see oral and mental starter).
- Write on the board all the answers shown. Ask for a few more suggestions if many answers are the same.
- Hopefully, 12 will have been given, and so the students should be asked what is special about this number. Emphasise that it is the **lowest common multiple** or **LCM**.
- Repeat for a common multiple of 4 and 5.
- Now ask for the lowest common multiple of 3 and 5.
- Then for the lowest common multiple of 4 and 6.
- Many students will answer 24, as they will have spotted that previous answers were the product of the two numbers in question.
- Make sure that they understand that 12 is the LCM of 4 and 6.
- The students should be encouraged to write out the multiples for the two numbers and to look for the first common value in each list. For example, for the LCM of 4 and 5:

$$4 \quad 8 \quad 12 \quad 16 \quad \textcircled{20} \quad 24 \quad 28 \quad \ldots$$
$$5 \quad 10 \quad 15 \quad \textcircled{20} \quad 25 \quad 30 \quad 35 \quad \ldots$$

- Now ask them to give a number that is a factor of 12 and a factor of 18.
- Once again, write on the board all the numbers shown. It is likely that all possibilities will be shown (1, 2, 3, 6) plus a few that are incorrect.
- Ensure that the class has grasped the concept and, if any factors are missing, ask what is needed to complete the set.
- Ask: 'What is special about 6?' Emphasise that it is the **highest common factor** or **HCF**.
- Repeat for the common factors of 30 and 50.
- Now ask for the highest common factor of 16 and 20.
- Repeat for 15 and 30. (5 is a likely answer here – make sure that they understand that the HCF is 15.)
- The students should be encouraged to write the factors and look for the highest common value.
- **The class can now do Exercise 1B from Pupil Book 1.**

© HarperCollins*Publishers* Ltd 2003

1 **a** 10, 4, 18, 8, 72, 100   **b** 18, 69, 81, 33, 72   **c** 10, 65, 100   **d** 10, 100
2 **a** 4, 8, 12, 16, 20, 24, 28, 32, 36, 40   **b** 5, 10, 15, 20, 25, 30, 35, 40, 45, 50
   c 8, 16, 24, 32, 40, 48, 56, 64, 72, 80   **d** 9, 18, 27, 36, 45, 54, 63, 72, 81, 90
   e 10, 20, 30, 40, 50, 60, 70, 80, 90, 100
3 **a** 1, 3, 5, 15   **b** 1, 2, 4, 5, 10, 20   **c** 1, 2, 4, 8, 16, 32   **d** 1, 2, 3, 4, 6, 12
   e 1, 5, 25
4 **a** 40   **b** 20   **c** 36   **d** 40
5 **a** 5   **b** 5   **c** 4   **d** 4
6 **a** 45   **b** 25   **c** 24   **d** 12   **e** 24   **f** 60   **g** 63   **h** 77
7 **a** 3   **b** 4   **c** 2   **d** 4   **e** 2   **f** 2   **g** 9   **h** 1

Extension Answers

36, 1225

Plenary

- Write numbers on the board (or use prepared cards), such as:
     1, 2, 3, 4, 6, 8, 10, 12, 15, 20, 24, 25, 30, 35, 40, 48
- Ask the students to pick out one number or card and then:
   • When a low-value is chosen, ask for the first ten multiples.
   • When a high-value is chosen, ask for all the factors.
- Then ask the students to pick out two numbers or cards. Ask for the LCM when both are low-values. Ask for the HCF when both are high-value, or ask for the product (or quotient and remainder) if one is high and one low.
- Alternatively, ask for a card that is the lowest common multiple of 5 and 6 or the highest common factor of 15 and 20, etc.

- multiple
- factor
- prime
- highest common factor (HCF)
- lowest common multiple (LCM)

Homework

1 Write out the first ten multiples of each of these.
   a 6   **b** 4   **c** 10   **d** 15   **e** 21
2 Write out the factors for each of these.
   a 16   **b** 15   **c** 20   **d** 8   **e** 12
3 Find the LCM of
   a 6 and 10   **b** 6 and 21   **c** 4 and 10   **d** 6 and 15
4 Find the HCF of
   a 16 and 20   **b** 15 and 20   **c** 8 and 12   **d** 6 and 10

Answers
 1 **a** 6, 12, 18, 24, 30, 36, 42, 48, 54, 60   **b** 4, 8, 12, 16, 20, 24, 28, 32, 36, 40
    c 10, 20, 30, 40, 50, 60, 70, 80, 90, 100   **d** 15, 30, 45, 60, 75, 90, 105, 120, 135, 150
    e 21, 42, 63, 84, 105, 126, 147, 168, 189, 210
 2 **a** 1, 2, 4, 8, 16   **b** 1, 3, 5, 15   **c** 1, 2, 4, 5, 10, 20   **d** 1, 2, 4, 8   **e** 1, 2, 3, 4, 6, 12
 3 **a** 30   **b** 42   **c** 20   **d** 30
 4 **a** 4   **b** 5   **c** 4   **d** 2

Framework objectives – Powers and roots

Use squares, positive and negative square roots, cubes and cube roots, and index notation for small positive integer powers.

Oral and mental starter

- Write on the board 4, 9 and 16. Invite the students to name these numbers.
- Some may identify them as square numbers.
- Make sure they understand why these are called square numbers by showing them how the numbers form square patterns of dots. Continue to introduce the class to square numbers up to 12 × 12.
- Reinforce this concept by stating that when we multiply any number by itself, the answer is called the square of the number or the number squared. This is because the answer is a square number.
- Now show the class the sequence of square numbers from 1 to 144. Then ask them, either as a class or individually, to read the sequence out.
- Try to get the class to memorise the sequence. Cover numbers in the sequence one or two at a time.
- Repeat for as long as necessary.

Main lesson activity

- Following on from the oral and mental starter, say to the class: '49 is a square number. Which number do you have to square to get 49?'
- It is likely that students will identify 7.
- Then move on to the concept that the opposite of the square number is its **square root**, represented by the symbol $\sqrt{\ }$. So, in this case, $\sqrt{49} = 7$.
- Ask for a few more examples such as $\sqrt{16}$, $\sqrt{36}$, $\sqrt{81}$ and $\sqrt{100}$.
- Write out a list of the square roots up to $\sqrt{144}$ or refer to the table in Pupil Book 1 page 6.
- Many students have difficulty recalling these, so get them to write the list in their books.

- **The class can now do Exercise 1C from Pupil Book 1.**

Exercise 1C Answers

1 $5^2 + 12^2 = 169 = 13^2$, $6^2 + 8^2 = 100 = 10^2$, $10^2 + 24^2 = 676 = 26^2$, $7^2 + 24^2 = 625 = 25^2$
2 **a** 4 **b** 6 **c** 2 **d** 7 **e** 1 **f** 3 **g** 10 **h** 9 **i** 5 **j** 8
3 **a** 6 **b** 4 **c** 3 **d** 120 **e** 15 **f** 21 **g** 90 **h** 15
4 **a** 17 **b** 31 **c** 23 **d** 50 **e** 36 **f** 27 **g** 57 **h** 19 **i** 63 **j** 42
5 **a** 16 **b** 33 **c** 25 **d** 52 **e** 38 **f** 29 **g** 59 **h** 21 **i** 64 **j** 45
6 **a** 17 **b** 22 **c** 14 **d** 21 **e** 3

Plenary

Key Words

☐ **square**
☐ **square root**
☐ **power**
☐ **index**

● Recapitulate the concept of square numbers and their square roots, including a reminder about root notation.

● Conduct a quick recall test of square numbers and square roots.

1 What is the square root of 64?

2 What is 10 squared?

3 What is 3 squared?

4 What is the square root of 81?

5 What is the square root of 100?

6 What is 5 squared?

7 What is the square root of 121?

8 What is 2 squared?

9 If $x^2 = 16$, what is the value of x?

10 What are the values of x if $x^2 = 25$?

Answers **1** 8 **2** 100 **3** 9 **4** 9 **5** 10 **6** 25 **7** 11 **8** 4 **9** 4 **10** 5

Homework

1 Without using a calculator, write down or work out each of these.

  a $\sqrt{25}$ **b** $\sqrt{49}$ **c** $\sqrt{16} \times \sqrt{25}$ **d** $\sqrt{64} \div \sqrt{16}$ **e** $\sqrt{81} \div \sqrt{9} \times \sqrt{36}$

2 Use a calculator to find the value of each of these.

  a $\sqrt{441}$ **b** $\sqrt{784}$ **c** $\sqrt{1024}$ **d** $\sqrt{1225}$ **e** $\sqrt{1681}$

Answers
  1 a 5 **b** 7 **c** 20 **d** 2 **e** 18
  2 a 21 **b** 28 **c** 32 **d** 35 **e** 41

Framework objectives – Prime factors

Find the prime factor decomposition of a number.

Oral and mental starter

- Using a target board like the one shown, point at a number and ask a student picked at random to give the factors of the number.
- Recall the rule for factors: that is, they occur in pairs.
- 1 and the number itself are always factors.
- A prime number has only two factors: itself and 1.
- Note that 1 is not a prime number, since it has only one factor – itself.

12	13	30	4	22
25	18	50	15	14
10	17	6	9	25
32	20	16	28	40

Main lesson activity

- Ask for the answer to $2 \times 3 \times 3$ (= 18).
- What about $2 \times 2 \times 5$ (=20), $3 \times 5 \times 5$ (= 75), $3 \times 3 \times 7$ (= 63)?
- Ask the class what can they tell you about the numbers in these multiplications? Establish that the numbers are all prime.
- This is the **prime factor form** of a number. That is, the number broken down into a product of primes.
- How can we find this if we start with 30, say?
- Explain the tree method. First, 30 is split into a product such as 2×15. Then any number in this product which is not a prime is split.
- Give another example: find the prime factors of 20.

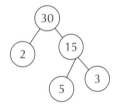

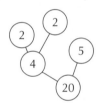

- Repeat with 36 ($2 \times 2 \times 3 \times 3$) and 60 ($2 \times 2 \times 3 \times 5$).
- **The class can now do Exercise 1D from Pupil Book 1.**

1 **a** 12 **b** 90 **c** 36 **d** 30 **e** 20
2 **a** $2 \times 2 \times 2$ **b** 2×5 **c** $2 \times 2 \times 2 \times 2$ **d** $2 \times 2 \times 5$ **e** $2 \times 2 \times 7$ **f** 2×17
   g 5×7 **h** $2 \times 2 \times 2 \times 5$ **i** $2 \times 5 \times 5$ **j** $2 \times 2 \times 5 \times 5$
3 **a** $2 \times 3 \times 7$ **b** $3 \times 5 \times 5$ **c** $2 \times 2 \times 5 \times 7$ **d** $2 \times 5 \times 5 \times 5$
   e $2 \times 2 \times 2 \times 2 \times 3 \times 5$ **f** $2 \times 2 \times 2 \times 3 \times 3$ **g** $2 \times 2 \times 2 \times 2 \times 2 \times 3$
   h $2 \times 2 \times 2 \times 2 \times 2 \times 2 \times 2 \times 2$

Plenary

- Choose a number, say 30.
- Call students to the board and ask them to find the factors (1, 2, 3, 5, 6, 10, 15, 30) and the prime factors ($2 \times 3 \times 5$).
- Choose another number, say 24, and repeat with the students. (The factors are 1, 2, 3, 4, 6, 8, 12, 24, and the prime factors are $2 \times 2 \times 2 \times 3$.)
- Choose two more numbers and repeat the activity.

Key Words

- factor
- prime
- highest common factor (HCF)
- lowest common multiple (LCM)
- powers

Homework

1   These are the prime factors of three numbers. What are the numbers?

   a $2 \times 3 \times 5$ **b** $2 \times 2 \times 3$ **c** $2 \times 2 \times 5 \times 5$

2   Using a prime factor tree, work out the prime factors of:

   a 24   **b** 80   **c** 45   **d** 60   **e** 18

Answers
   1 **a** 30 **b** 12 **c** 100
   2 **a** $2 \times 2 \times 2 \times 3$ **b** $2 \times 2 \times 2 \times 2 \times 5$ **c** $3 \times 3 \times 5$ **d** $2 \times 2 \times 3 \times 5$ **e** $2 \times 3 \times 3$

Framework objectives – Sequences 1

Generate and describe integer sequences. Generate terms of a linear sequence using term-to-term definition of the sequence.

Oral and mental starter

- This activity can be played as a game between two teams.
- Ask a student to give the first two terms of a sequence. For example: 1, 5.
- Ask another student (from the other team, if a game is played) to continue the sequence. For example: 1, 5, 9. Then another (from the first team) to continue the sequence. For example: 1, 5, 9, 13, ...
- Once it becomes obvious that there is a well-defined sequence, stop and ask another student to give the first two terms of a different sequence and so on. (Alternate the starting team.)
- Points are scored under the following conditions:
  - Once you decide a sequence is obvious, a student from the starting team has to describe the rule.
  - At any time, students from the opposing team may challenge the last student to justify the term they have given. A point is scored if the term is wrong or the rule is incorrect.
  - A student is unable to carry on the sequence (other team scores).
- Do not allow bizarre rules, although students should be encouraged to make sequences hard to spot. For example: 1, 5, 25 (× 5), or 1, 2, 3, 5, 8 (Fibonacci), or 98, 97, 95, 92, ... (subtract 1, 2, 3, ...).
- If a score is kept, do not declare a winning team yet.

Main lesson activity

- Write some sequences on the board such as:
  2, 5, 8, 11, 14, ...   4, 8, 16, 32, 64, ...   100, 99, 97, 94, 90, ...
- Ask the class to describe how each one is building up, that is: 'What is the rule?' Ask them what the next two terms are.
- Invite the students to make up their own number sequences. (If number cards are available, the students can lay out their patterns on the desk.)
- Go round the class and pick some sequences to write on the board.
- When at least five sequences have been collected, ask the rest of the class to say what the next two terms are and also to describe the rule for developing the sequence. Introduce the idea of a term-to-term rule.
- Draw (or have on an OHT) this flow diagram:

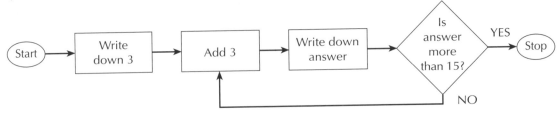

- Briefly explain the parts of the diagram: start/stop box (oval), action box (rectangle), decision box (diamond).
- Work through the diagram to give the multiples of 3 up to 18: 3, 6, 9, 12, 15, 18.

- **The class can now do Exercise 1E from Pupil Book 1.**

1 **a** 3, 8, 13, 18, 23, 28, 33, 38, 43   **b** 2, 4, 6, 8, 10, 12, 14, 16, 18, 20, 22
  c 10, 100, 1000, 10 000, 100 000, 1 000 000, 10 000 000

2 **a** Even numbers   **b** Same as **1b** with ⌈ Write down 1 ⌉

3 **a** Powers of 10   **b** Same as **1c** with ⌈ Write down 2 ⌉ and ⌈ Multiply by 2 ⌉

4 **a** Goes up by 3   **b** Multiply by 4   **c** Increases by 3, 4, 5, 6, 7, ...
  d Goes up by 3, 5, 7, 9, ...
6 **a** Increases 1, 2, 3, 4, 5, ... 61, 68   **b** Goes down 1, 2, 3, 4, ... 69, 62
  c Increases 2, 4, 6, 8, 10, ... 43, 57   **d** Increases 4, 6, 8, 10, 12, ... 56, 72
7 **a ii** 25, 36, 49, 64   **b ii** 15, 21, 28, 36   **c ii** 16, 32, 64, 128
  d ii 30, 42, 56, 72

Square numbers and triangle numbers

Plenary

Key Words

- Repeat the introductory activity, but this time *you* start the sequences and use the same two starting numbers until no more sequences can be suggested. For example:
    1, 2, 4, 8, ...   1, 2, 3, 4, ...   1, 2, 4, 7, 11, 16, ...   1, 2, 5, 10, 17, ...
    1, 3, 9, 27, ...   1, 3, 5, 7, 9, ...   1, 3, 6, 10, ...   1, 3, 7, 13, ...
- Ask the students to describe each term-to-term rule.
- If a score has been kept from the oral and mental starter, this can be used to decide the winning team.

sequence
term
rule
flow diagram
generate
consecutive

Homework

1 Write down four sequences beginning 1, 2, ... Explain how each of them is generated.

2 Describe how each of the following sequences is generated and write down the next two terms
   a 50, 48, 46, 44, 42, 40, ...   **b** 9, 12, 18, 27, 39, 54, ...   **c** 1, 3, 6, 10, 15, 21, ...
   d 2, 6, 8, 14, 22, 36, ...

Answers
   2 **a** Decreases by 2; 38, 36   **b** Increases by 3, 6, 9, 12, 15, ...; 72, 93
     c Increases by 2, 3, 4, 5, ...; 28, 36   **d** Add previous two terms; 58, 94

LESSON 1.6

Framework objectives – Sequences 2

Begin to use linear expressions to describe the *n*th term of an arithmetic sequence, and justify its form by referring to the activity or practical context from which it was generated.

Generate terms of a linear sequence using term-to-term and position-to-term definitions of the sequence, on paper and using a spreadsheet or graphical calculator.

Oral and mental starter

- Explain to the class that they have to make you say a number: for example, 25.
- They do this by giving you a starting number. You apply a secret rule to it and respond with the number. For example, if the rule is 'Add 2', the students may say 7 and you reply 9. They say 16 and you reply 18. Then eventually, a student will say 23, to which you reply 25.
- This is a fairly easy rule. Other rules (and the answer to make you say 25) are: Square, 5; 3*n* + 1, 8; Multiply by 5, 5.
- To tie in with the main lesson activity the rules should be of the type $ax \pm b$.

Main lesson activity

- Ask the class: 'Given a term-to-term rule, can you generate the sequence?'
- 'The first term is 5 and the term-to-term rule is add 3 to the previous term. What sequence is found?'
- Show the class how to generate 5, 8, 11, 14, 17, …
- Give some other examples: first term 1, multiply each term by 5 (1, 5, 25, 125, 625, …); first term 2, multiply by 3 (2, 6, 18, 54, 162, …).
- Generate some sequences with more complex term-to-term rules. For example: first term 4, add 1 to the previous term and multiply by 2, which gives:
    $$4, (4 + 1) \times 2 = 10, (10 + 1) \times 2 = 22, …$$
- Discuss the difference between the term-to-term definition of a sequence and the position-to-term definition (see starter). For example, in the first sequence above, any term is given by multiplying the term position by 3 and adding 2.
- Demonstrate that this rule works. The first term is $3 \times 1 + 2 = 5$, the second term is $3 \times 2 + 2 = 8$, and the third term is $3 \times 3 + 2 = 11$.
- Show the class how to write this rule. 3 × term position + 2, which can be shortened to $3n + 2$. This is the position-to-term algebraic definition, which gives the *n*th term of the sequence.
- Give further examples. Each term of a sequence is given by $2n - 1$. What are the first five terms of the sequence? The answer is:
    $$2 \times 1 - 1 = 1, 2 \times 2 - 1 = 3, 2 \times 3 - 1 = 5, 2 \times 4 - 1 = 7, 2 \times 5 - 1 = 9$$
- Each term of a sequence is given by $4n + 4$. What are the first five terms of the sequence? The answer is:
    $$4 \times 1 + 4 = 8, 4 \times 2 + 4 = 12, 4 \times 3 + 4 = 16, 4 \times 4 + 4 = 20,$$
    $$4 \times 5 + 4 = 24$$

- **The class can now do Exercise 1F from Pupil Book 1**

1 **a** $a = 4, d = 5$ **b** $a = 1, d = 2$ **c** $a = 3, d = 6$ **d** $a = 5, d = -2$
2 **a** 1, 8, 15, 22, 29, 36, ... **b** 3, 5, 7, 9, 11, 13, ... **c** 5, 9, 13, 17, 21, 25, ...
   d 0.5, 2, 3.5, 5, 6.5, 8, ... **e** 4, 1, -2, -5, -8, -11, ... **f** 2, 1.5, 1, 0.5, 0, -0.5, ...
3 **a** 3, 6, 12, 24, 48 **b** 4, 13, 40, 121, 364 **c** 5, 8, 14, 26, 50
4 **a** 1, 3, 5, 7, 9 **b** 4, 7, 10, 13, 16 **c** 6, 10, 14, 18, 22 **d** 5, 7, 9, 11, 13
5 **a** 5, 9, 13, 17, 21 **b** 5, 8, 11, 14, 17 **c** 1, 4, 7, 10, 13 **d** 3, 5, 7, 9, 11

Plenary

Key Words

- Put a sequence on the board, such as 4, 6, 8, 10, 12, ...
- Discuss how to find the 100th term of the sequence.
- Some students may give a position-to-term definition:
   $2 \times$ term position $+ 2 = (2n + 2) = 202$
- Others may realise that it is the first term, 4, plus $99 \times 2 = 202$.
- Repeat with other sequences, such as 3, 7, 11, 15, 19, ... or 5, 7, 9, 11, 13, ...
- Demonstrate both the term-to-term definition and the position-to-term definition of these sequences.

- arithmetic sequence
- constant difference
- first term
- *n*th term

Homework

1 Given the first term a and the constant difference d, write down the first six terms of each of these sequences.

   a $a = 2, d = 6$ **b** $a = 5, d = 2$ **c** $a = 8, d = -3$

2 The *n*th term of a sequence is given by each of the rules below. Use each rule to write down the first five terms of each sequence.

   a $6n - 1$ **b** $10n + 3$

Answers
   1 **a** 2, 8, 14, 20, 26, 32 **b** 5, 7, 9, 11, 13, 15 **c** 8, 5, 2, -1, -4, -7
   2 **a** 5, 11, 17, 23, 29 **b** 13, 23, 33, 43, 53

LESSON 1.7

Framework objectives – Solving problems

Solve more demanding problems and investigate in a range of contexts: algebra

Solve more complex problems by breaking them into smaller steps or tasks, choosing and using efficient techniques for calculation, algebraic manipulation and graphical representation.

Oral and mental starter

- There is no starter, as the investigations take considerable time to set up and do.

Main lesson activity

- This is a lesson on investigations, building on work done in Year 7, such as 'Mathematical mice'. The objective is to concentrate on breaking down a problem into easier, more manageable steps. There are two problems in the exercise.
- The main activity is to go through the problem first encountered at the start of the last section, Sequences 2.
- This is outlined in Pupil Book 1 and reproduced here.

At the start of the last section you were asked to say how many 1 metre square slabs would be needed to go round a $100 \times 100 \, m^2$ pond.
To solve this problem you need to:

Step 1   Break down the problem into simple stages.
Step 2   Set up a table of results.
Step 3   Predict and test a rule.
Step 4   Use your rule to answer the question.

Step 1   This has been done already with the diagrams given.

Step 2

Pond size	Number of slabs
1	8
2	12
3	16
4	20

Step 3   Use the table to spot how the sequence is growing.
In this case, it is increasing by 4 each time.
So, a $5 \times 5 \, m^2$ pond will need 24 slabs.
Show this by a sketch (as shown on the right).
We see that the number of slabs (S) is 4 times the side length of the pond (P) plus 4, which we can write as:
$$S = 4P + 4$$

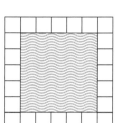

Step 4   Now apply the rule to the $100 \times 100 \, m^2$ pond, where $P = 100$:
$$S = 4 \times 100 + 4 = 404$$
So, 404 slabs will be needed.

- **The class can now try the investigations in Exercise 1G of Pupil Book 1.**

SATs Answers

1 **a** 4   **b** 24   **c** 36   **d** 10
2 **a** 305, 311   **b** 36, 49   **c** Square numbers, whose differences are 3, 5, 7, ...
3 **a** 64 grey and 4 black   **b** 256 grey and 4 black
5 **a** The number of grey tiles   **b** 1 black and 36 grey

Plenary

Key Words

- investigation
- table
- simpler case
- rule
- test
- predict

- There is no plenary to this lesson, although if desired one or more solutions to the problems in Exercise 1G could be discussed.
- When discussing the problems, invite the students to present their investigation methods and their findings.

Homework

Write up one of the investigations for a wall display. Include the following:

- The problem
- Your working
- The table of results
- Your rule
- The answer

Shape, Space and Measures 1

Framework Objectives – Parallel and perpendicular lines

Use correctly the vocabulary, notation and labelling conventions for lines and angles.

Identify parallel and perpendicular lines.

Oral and mental starter

- Use a target board, such as the one shown. This activity can be repeated using different sets of numbers or different rules, but the theme is supplementary and complementary angles (which sum to 180° and 90°, respectively).

90	70	50	30	60	58	73
45	105	32	17	127	15	165
63	87	25	120	148	20	3
163	135	75	110	130	65	40

- Ask the students to choose a number from the board, and subtract it from 180.
- Ask the students to find two numbers that add up to 180.
- Ask the students to add two numbers together to give a total less than 180, and subtract the result from 180.
- Ask the students to find two numbers that add up to 90.
- Ask the students to find three numbers that add up to 180.

Main lesson activity

- Draw two parallel lines on the board.
- Explain to the class that the two lines are **parallel**. This means that they will never meet, no matter how far they are extended in either direction. Show them how parallel lines are indicated by using the arrow notation.

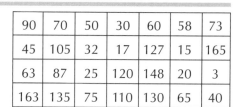

- Ask the class to give some everyday examples where they might see parallel lines. Some possibilities are lined paper, railings and railway tracks.
- Now draw two perpendicular lines on the board.
- Explain to the class that the two lines are **perpendicular** and meet at 90°. This is also called a **right angle**. Show them how a right angle is indicated by drawing on a square corner.
- Ask the class to give some everyday examples where they might see perpendicular lines. Some possibilities are the lines on graph paper and the corner of a picture frame.

- **The class can now do Exercise 2A from Pupil Book 1.**

1 a, c, e, g
3 a, b, f, h
4 **a** YZ   **b** PQ and RS
   c CD is perpendicular to AC and BD

2 The two lines are parallel

Plenary

Key Words

● Ask the class to explain the properties of parallel lines and perpendicular lines by sketching examples of each on the board.

☐ **parallel**
☐ **perpendicular**
☐ **right angle**
☐ **sketch**

Homework

1 Write down which of the following sets of lines are parallel.

   a   **b**   **c**   **d**

2 Draw a line AB that is 5 cm long. Draw another line CD that is also 5 cm long and is parallel to AB.

3 Write down which of the following lines are perpendicular.

   a   **b**   **c**   **d**

4 Copy and complete the following.

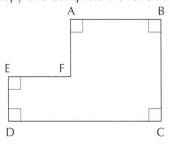

   a AF is parallel to the lines _____ and _____

   b DE is perpendicular to the lines _____ and _____ and _____

Answers
 1 **a** and **c**
 3 **b** and **c**
 4 **a** BC and DE   **b** CD and EF and AB

Framework Objectives – Measuring and drawing angles

Use angle measure; distinguish between and estimate the size of acute, obtuse and reflex angles.

Use a ruler and protractor to measure and draw angles, including reflex angles, to the nearest degree.

Oral and mental starter

- Draw a table on the board as shown below. Ask the class to tell you how many of each type of angle each shape has, and also any special properties of the shape.
- Fill in the table.
- For different triangles and quadrilaterals, for example, instead of writing the word in the left column, insert a sketch.

	Acute	Obtuse	Right angles	Special properties
Equilateral triangle				
Square				
Rectangle				
Parallelogram				
(triangle sketch)	2	2	0	One pair of parallel sides

- You could reverse the problem by inserting numbers or properties in the table and asking the class for the name or a sketch of the shape (as on the final row).
- Extend the table or change the column labels to facts about sides in order to extend the task.

Main lesson activity

- Explain to the class that this lesson will remind them how to measure and draw angles using a protractor and ruler.
- Draw on the board these four different types of angle, with their definitions. These can be copied into the students' books.

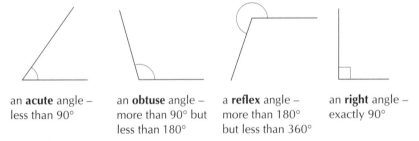

an **acute** angle – less than 90°

an **obtuse** angle – more than 90° but less than 180°

a **reflex** angle – more than 180° but less than 360°

an **right** angle – exactly 90°

- Remind the class how to measure acute and obtuse angles (to the nearest degree) using a protractor and ruler.
- Show the class how to measure the size of a reflex angle by first measuring the interior angle and then subtracting this angle from 360°.
- Ask the class to draw some reflex angles in their books and then to measure the size of each angle.
- This activity can also be done using a full circular protractor, which many students find much easier to use.

- **The class can now do Exercise 2B from Pupil Book 1.**

Key Words

- acute angle
- obtuse angle
- reflex angle
- protractor

Plenary

- Draw on the board various acute, obtuse and reflex angles and ask the class to estimate the size of each one.

Homework

1 Write down whether each of the following angles is acute, obtuse or reflex.

a   b   c   d   e   f

2 Measure the size of each of the following angles, giving your answer to the nearest degree.

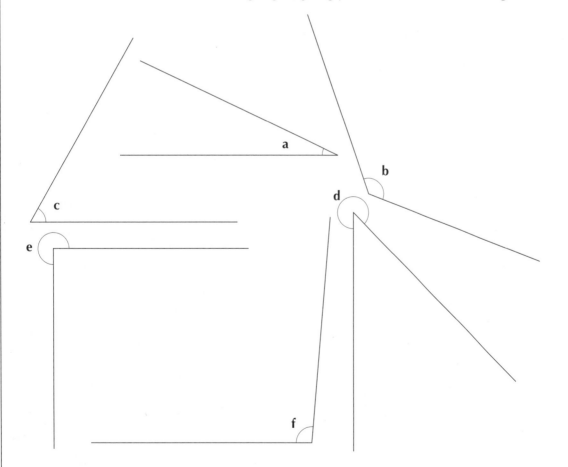

3 Draw and label each of the following angles.

a 20°   **b** 48°   **c** 140°   **d** 108°   **e** 210°   **f** 302°   **g** 90°

Answers
1 **a** obtuse **b** acute **c** reflex **d** obtuse **e** reflex **f** acute
2 **a** 25° **b** 130° **c** 60° **d** 315° **e** 270° **f** 95° (accept angles ± 1°)
3 Angles correct and 90° labelled with square corner

LESSON 2.3

Oral and mental starter

- Imagine two equilateral triangles of the same size.
- Place them together, edge to edge.
- Ask the class to give the name of the shape that is formed (a rhombus).
- Ask them to explain why the answer is always the same (the same shape is formed no matter which edges are placed together).
- This can be repeated using three or four equilateral triangles.

Main lesson activity

- Remind the class how to calculate angles at a point and angles on a straight line, by working through the following two examples:
- **Sum of the angles around a point** $a + b + c = 360°$

For example, calculate the size of angle a.
$$a = 360° - 160° - 120°$$
$$a = 80°$$

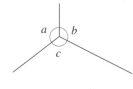

- **Sum of the angles on a straight line** $a + b + c = 180°$

For example, calculate the size of angle b.
$$b = 180° - 80° - 40°$$
$$b = 60°$$

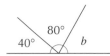

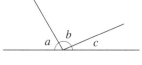

- Use the following activity to establish the sum of the interior angles in a triangle and work through some calculations using this result.
- **Practical work for students**
  Coloured, gummed squares are required.
  1 Draw a triangle on a gummed square and clearly mark each angle with a letter.
  2 Cut out the triangle and tear off the three angles.
  3 Stick each angle on a piece of paper so that the three angles are around a common point.
  4 Ask the class to write down what this shows.
- **Sum of the interior angles of a triangle** $a + b + c = 180°$

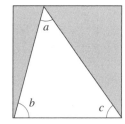

- Now go over the properties of vertically opposite angles.
- **Vertically opposite angles** $a = d$ and $b = c$
  Vertically opposite angles are also called just **opposite angles**.
  Notice that the adjacent angles add up to 180°:
  $$a + b = 180°$$

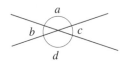

- **The class can now do Exercise 2C from Pupil Book 1.**

Key Words

- [ ] angles at a point
- [ ] angles on a straight line
- [ ] angles in a triangle
- [ ] vertically opposite angles

Plenary

● Ask some students to explain the meaning of: angles around a point, angles on a line, angles in a triangle and vertically opposite angles.
● Ask others to make up an example to illustrate each of the above.

Homework

1 Calculate the size of each unknown angle.

a   b 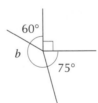   c

2 Calculate the size of each unknown angle.

a 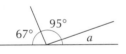   b   c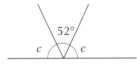

3 Calculate the size of each unknown angle.

a 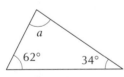   b 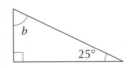   c

4 Calculate the size of each unknown angle.

a 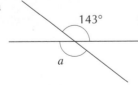   b 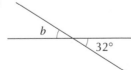   c

Answers
1 a 200° b 135° c 99°
2 a 18° b 62° c 64°
3 a 84° b 65° c 102°
4 a 143° b 32° c 46°

LESSON 2.4

Framework objectives – The geometric properties of quadrilaterals

Solve geometrical problems using side and angle properties of special quadrilaterals, explaining reasoning with diagrams and text.

Classify quadrilaterals by their geometric properties.

Investigate in a range of contexts: shape and space.

Oral and mental starter

- This is mainly a revision exercise on quadrilaterals.
- Tell the class to imagine a quadrilateral that has only two lines of symmetry:
  Ask a pupil to draw one possible shape on the board with its name;
  Ask another pupil to draw another example that is possible.
  (The possible shapes are a rectangle and a rhombus.)
- Now tell the class that the shape has equal sides, and ask them which of the two quadrilaterals satisfies both conditions (the rhombus does).
- This activity can be repeated using different quadrilaterals.

Main lesson activity

Explain to the class that the lesson is about looking at the properties of all the special quadrilaterals. Draw each of the following shapes on the board or on an overhead projector (OHP). Write down the geometric properties of the square. Now ask the class to describe the geometric properties of each of the other shapes. Write down all the properties of each shape below and tell the pupils to copy these into their books.

Square
- Four equal sides
- Four right angles
- Opposite sides parallel
- Diagonals bisect each other at right angles
- Four lines of symmetry
- Rotational symmetry of order four

Rectangle
- Two pairs of equal sides
- Four right angles
- Opposite sides parallel
- Diagonals bisect each other
- Two lines of symmetry
- Rotational symmetry of order two

Parallelogram
- Two pairs of equal sides
- Two pairs of equal angles
- Opposite sides parallel
- Diagonals bisect each other
- No lines of symmetry
- Rotational symmetry of order two

Rhombus
- Four equal sides
- Two pairs of equal angles
- Opposite sides parallel
- Diagonals bisect each other at right angles
- Two lines of symmetry
- Rotational symmetry of order two

Kite
- Two pairs of adjacent sides of equal length
- One pair of equal angles
- Diagonals intersect at right angles
- One line of symmetry

Arrowhead or Delta
- Two pairs of adjacent sides of equal length
- One pair of equal angles
- Diagonals intersect at right angles outside the shape
- One line of symmetry

Trapezium
- One pair of parallel sides
- Some trapeziums have one line of symmetry

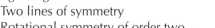

● The class can now do Exercise 2D from Pupil Book 1.

Exercise 2D Answers

1

No lines of symmetry	One line of symmetry	Two lines of symmetry	Four lines of symmetry
Parallelogram Trapezium	Kite Arrowhead	Rectangle Rhombus	Square

Note Trapezium sometimes has one line of symmetry

2

Rotational symmetry of order one	Rotational symmetry of order two	Rotational symmetry of order four
Kite Arrowhead Trapezium	Rectangle Parallelogram Rhombus	Square

3 Rectangle
4 Parallelogram
5 Wrong, it could be a rhombus
6 Wrong, it could be a parallelogram or a rhombus
7 **a** Parallelogram, rhombus **b** parallelogram **c** parallelogram

Key Words

☐ **bisect**
☐ **diagonal**
☐ **quadrilateral**
☐ **square**
☐ **rectangle**
☐ **parallelogram**
☐ **rhombus**
☐ **kite**
☐ **arrowhead**
☐ **delta**
☐ **trapezium**

Plenary

● Ask individual pupils to draw on the board one of the special quadrilaterals they have met during the lesson and then explain to the rest of the class all the geometric properties of the shape they have chosen.

Homework

1 Copy and complete the table:

	Square	Rectangle	Parallelogram	Rhombus
Number of lines of symmetry	4			
Order of rotational symmetry		2		
All sides equal			No	
All angles equal				No
Opposite sides parallel	Yes			

2 a Which quadrilaterals have diagonals that bisect each other?

b Which quadrilaterals have diagonals that intersect at right angles?

3 The instructions below are to draw the rectangle shown.

REPEAT TWICE
[FORWARD 5
TURN RIGHT 90°
FORWARD 12
TURN RIGHT 90°]

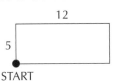

Write down a set of similar instructions to draw a rectangle that has sides twice the length of those on the diagram.

Answers

1

	Square	Rectangle	Parallelogram	Rhombus
Number of lines of symmetry	4	2	0	2
Order of rotational symmetry	4	2	2	2
All sides equal	Yes	No	No	Yes
All angles equal	Yes	Yes	No	No
Opposite sides parallel	Yes	Yes	Yes	Yes

2 a square, rectangle, parallelogram, rhombus **b** square, rhombus, kite, arrowhead
3 REPEAT TWICE, [FORWARD 10, TURN RIGHT 90°, FORWARD 24, TURN RIGHT 90°]

LESSON 2.5

Framework objectives – Constructions

Use a ruler and protractor to construct a triangle given two sides and the included angle (SAS) or two angles and the included side (ASA).

Oral and mental starter

- Geometric acronyms.
- Write on the board, '180 DIAT'. Explain to the class that this is an acronym for 180 degrees in a triangle.
- Ask the class to try to solve the following acronyms. They refer to some of the properties they have looked at in the last two lessons.
  - 90 DIARA (90 degrees in a right angle)
  - 180 DOASL (180 degrees on a straight line)
  - 360 DIACT (360 degrees in a complete turn)
  - 3 SIAT (three sides in a triangle)
  - 4 SIAQ (four sides in a quadrilateral)
- Ask the class to make up some of their own geometric acronyms.

Main teaching activity

- This lesson revises the Year 7 work on constructing triangles. It will also help students to consolidate their line and angle drawing skills.
- Remind the class how to construct a triangle accurately from information given on a sketch as follows.

- **To construct a triangle, given two sides and the included angle (SAS)**
- Draw a sketch of such a triangle on the board.
- The aim is to construct the triangle so that all the given measurements are exact.
- Remind the class that the angles are measured to the nearest degree and the sides to the nearest millimetre.
- Ask the students to draw the triangle in stages as follows:
  - Draw line BC 9 cm long.
  - Draw an angle of 55° at C.
  - Draw AC 6 cm long.
  - Join AB to complete the triangle.

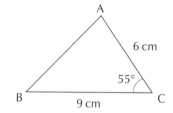

- **To construct a triangle given two angles and the included side (ASA)**
- Draw a sketch of such a triangle on the board.
- Ask the students to draw the triangle in stages as follows:
  - Draw line YZ 7 cm long.
  - Draw an angle of 40° at Y.
  - Draw an angle of 60° at Z.
  - Extend both angle lines to intersect at X to complete the triangle.

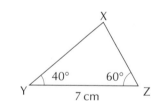

- Tell the class always to label the known sides and angles, and to leave any construction lines and marks on their completed diagrams.
- ICT facilities can be used for one extra lesson to explore how triangles can be drawn using computer software packages such as LOGO.

- **The class can now do Exercise 2E from Pupil Book 1.**

Plenary

● Briefly summarise the two constructions covered during the lesson.
● Point out that only three pieces of information are required to construct any triangle accurately.

Homework

1 Construct each of the following triangles. Remember to label all the lines and angles. The triangles are not drawn to scale.

a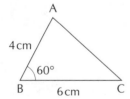

b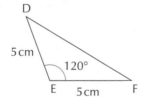

2 Construct each of the following triangles. Remember to label all the lines and angles. The triangles are not drawn to scale.

a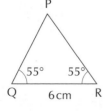

b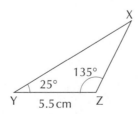

3 Construct the triangle ABC with AB = 6 cm, angle A = 40° and angle B = 50°.

Handling Data 1

Framework objectives – Probability
Use the vocabulary of probability when interpreting the results of an experiment.
Appreciate that random processes are unpredictable.

Oral and mental starter

R	R	R	R	R
B	B	B	G	G

R	R	R	R	B
G	G	G	Y	Y

- Use two boards marked with grids, as shown on the right.
- The letters could be replaced by colours: R, red; B, blue; G, green; Y, yellow.
- Hold up the first grid and ask the students which colour there is most of, and which there is least of.
- Now repeat with the second grid.
- You could now increase the level of difficulty by putting one grid beneath the other, as shown, and making the colours out of 20. Then, by covering columns, there could be 16 colours, say, and so on.
- Write the following words, in random order, on the board.

    Impossible   Very unlikely   Unlikely   Even chance   Likely   Very likely
    Certain

    Ask the class to give you a sentence using these words. For example:
    'There is an even chance of picking red for the first grid.'
    'It is impossible to pick yellow for the second grid.'
- Repeat for each colour on each grid.

Main lesson activity

- Explain that the lesson is about chance and using the words associated with probability.
- Draw on the board a probability scale with five, equally spaced, dividing marks plus the two end-of-line numbers. Do not label them.
- Write one word on the scale: for example, 'Impossible'.
- Ask the class to tell you where the words listed above fit onto the scale.
- Now ask them to think of events that are impossible. Discuss the idea that some things are almost impossible, but could still happen.
- Try to encourage them to give you events that are both mathematical and non-mathematical.
- Use the key words when talking about their answers.

- **The class can now do Exercise 3A from Pupil Book 1.**

Plenary

● Point out that different words are sometimes used to mean the same thing (e.g. fifty–fifty chance and even chance).
● Reinforce to the class that the work they have done is often based on experiments or expectation and therefore the results, although probably reliable, may not happen every time.
● Tell them that the next step will be to use the number scale rather than words.

Key Words

☐ **event**
☐ **impossible**
☐ **unlikely**
☐ **likely**
☐ **even chance**

Homework

1 A bag contains 10 counters. How many red counters are in the bag if the chance of picking out a red counter is:

   a even?   **b** impossible?   **c** certain?

2 Ten cards are numbered from 1 to 10. Describe in words the chance of picking:

   a an odd number   **b** a number less than 11   **c** a number greater than 3

3 A bag contains 10 counters. It is impossible to pick a red counter. There is an even chance that a blue counter is picked. One counter is yellow. There is twice the chance of picking a green counter than a yellow counter. The rest of the counters are purple.

   How many red, blue, green and purple counters are there?

   Answers
   1 a 5 **b** 0 **c** 10
   2 a Even **b** Certain **c** Likely or very likely
   3 a No red, five blue, two green, two purple

LESSON
3.2

Framework objectives – Probability scales

Know that if the probability of an event occurring is p, then the probability of it not occurring is $1 - p$.

Oral and mental starter

- Write ten numbers on the board or on an OHT. Tell the class to try to memorise as many as possible. Give them about 15 seconds.
- Now cover the numbers up and see how many numbers the students can recall. This could be a timed exercise, which could be repeated in another lesson.
- Now write ten fractions and/or decimals on the board or on the OHT.
- Again, see how many the students can recall after, say, 20 seconds.
- This time, return to the ten fractions and/or decimals and ask the class what is needed to make each one add up to 1. Write the correct answer on the board or the OHT. To help them, you may wish to use a number line drawn on the board or a 'counting stick' with 10 divisions marked on. Mark it at one end with 0 and at the other end with 1.

0   1

- Tell the students that they now have 30 seconds to memorise the answers.

Main lesson activity

- Ask the class to tell you some events that are opposite or exclusive of each other. You may need to give them an example, such as red playing card, black playing card.
- Now give them an event and ask them what the opposite is: for example, even number, odd number, wears glasses, doesn't wear glasses.
- Now ask one student to give you a probability as a decimal and ask another student for the probability of that event not happening. This could be repeated several times.
- This could now be repeated with simple fractions.
- In pairs, students could now test each other by making up their own probabilities in turn, and writing them into two columns in their books.
- Introduce the idea that we say the probability of something happening is p, so the expression for the probability of its *not* happening is $1 - p$.
- Remind the class of the method used to calculate probabilities (introduced in Year 7):

$$\text{Probability of an event } (P) = \frac{\text{Number of outcomes in the event}}{\text{Total number of all possible outcomes}}$$

- **The class can now do Exercise 3B from Pupil Book 1.**

1 A' at 0.8, B' at 0.7, C' at 0.4, D' at 0.
2 0.8, 0.7, 0.4, 0, $\frac{3}{4}, \frac{2}{3}, \frac{1}{4}$
3 a $\frac{1}{10}$ b $\frac{9}{10}$ c $\frac{1}{2}$ d $\frac{1}{2}$ e $\frac{3}{10}$ f $\frac{7}{10}$ g $\frac{1}{5}$ h $\frac{4}{5}$
4 a $\frac{1}{4}$ b $\frac{3}{5}$ c $\frac{3}{4}$ d 0 e $\frac{3}{4}$ f $\frac{2}{5}$ g $\frac{1}{4}$ h 1
5 a $\frac{3}{4}$ b 8 c 24

Plenary

- Remind the class that they should never have an answer greater than 1.
- Point out that sometimes decimals are easier to use and at other times fractions are easier.
- Look at the problem of tossing two coins and obtaining at least one Head. Ask them to explain what we mean by 'at least one'. Now point out that 'at least one' is the opposite of 'none', so there are two approaches to this type of question, but the quicker way is to use $1 - \frac{1}{4}$.

Key Words

- probability
- event
- outcome
- random

Homework

1 The probabilities of different events happening are given below. Write down the probability of these events **not** happening:

a 0.1   b 0.25   c 0.5   d 0.6   e 0.85   f 0.91   g 0.001

h 1   i $\frac{1}{5}$ j $\frac{1}{4}$ k $\frac{1}{10}$ l $\frac{2}{3}$ m $\frac{9}{10}$ n $\frac{4}{7}$

2 There are eight outcomes when throwing three coins. Make a list of all the outcomes. Write down the probability of obtaining:

a three Heads   b at least one Tail   c three Tails   d at least one Head

Answers
1 a 0.9 b 0.75 c 0.5 d 0.4 e 0.15 f 0.09 g 0.999 h 0 i $\frac{4}{5}$ j $\frac{3}{4}$ k $\frac{9}{10}$ l $\frac{1}{3}$ m $\frac{1}{10}$ n $\frac{3}{7}$
2 HHH, HHT, HTH, THH, HTT, THT, TTH, TTT
  a $\frac{1}{8}$ b $\frac{7}{8}$ c $\frac{1}{8}$ d $\frac{7}{8}$

Framework objectives – Collecting data

Collect data from a simple experiment and record in a frequency table. Estimate probabilities based on this data.

Oral and mental starter

- Write five colours on the board or on an OHT.
- Ask the students each to choose one of the colours but not to reveal it. They could write them down on a show-me board.
- Now ask them to hold up their boards to reveal their colours.
- Count up each colour.
- Ask the class how you could record these results.
- Encourage them to suggest alternative methods: for example, tally charts, just counting and recording the frequencies.
- Ask the class if they think that some colours are more popular than others and ask them for a reason. It could be that students chose their favourite colours even though you did not ask for this.
- Now lead on to probability by asking the students to predict the colour someone entering the room would choose.
- Point out that although the most popular colour has the best chance of being chosen, the person may choose one of the others.

Main lesson activity

- Ask the class to look at the table in Example 3.9.
- Point out that this is one way of recording data from an experiment.
- A different way would be to use tallies.
- Remind the students that they will often be asked to criticise an experiment. One common criticism is that there were not enough trials.
- Again remind them that experimental results may be unreliable.
- Now ask them to explain the word 'fair'. Discuss the meaning in the context of a dice or a spinner.
- Introduce the word 'bias'. Encourage the students to associate the words 'fair' and 'biased' (not fair).
- **The class can now do Exercise 3C from Pupil Book 1.**

Each question in this exercise consists of some practical work followed by recording using tallies or tables. So, the results of each student may be different.

Plenary

Key Words

- Reinforce the concept that when recording data, it is important to summarise results using totals (frequency table).
- Point out that when the students are collecting data, it is advisable to try to collect at least 30 pieces of information and preferably 50. However, this is not always practical.
- Briefly point out that the data that they have been collecting is called **primary data**.

- event
- trial
- frequency table
- experiment
- chance
- outcome
- probability

Homework

1 Toss a coin 30 times.

   a Record your results in a table.

   b Comment on whether you think the coin is fair or biased.

2 Conduct a survey of the colours of 50 cars on three roads near your home.

   a Record the results in the table shown below.

   b Write a brief report based on your results.

Make of car	Number of cars of each colour					
	Red	Green	Blue	Yellow	Black	Another colour

Homework Answers

   1 **a** A tally/frequency table recording Heads and Tails with a total of 30
   b If results are similar, the coin is fair. If results are quite different, the coin is not fair.

Framework objectives – Events

Find and justify probabilities based on equally likely outcomes in simple contexts.

Oral and mental starter

- Write on the board the following words, phrases and numbers:

    probability   dice   1   2   3   4   5   6   even   odd   spinner   blue
    green   3 red sections and 1 green section

- Ask the class to give you a sentence involving chance or probability that uses at least three of the words in the list. For example:

    'The probability of a spinner landing on blue is zero.'

- Now ask them to explain how the sentence could be true. For example:

    'There are no blue sections on the spinner so it is impossible.'

- Repeat this a few times. You may wish to change the list of words or insist that the sentence begins with 'The probability …'.

- If this proves difficult, the starter could be simplified by asking the class to complete sentences for you. For example:

    'The probability that a dice land on an even number is …'

Main lesson activity

- Tell the class about the person who wanted to buy a yacht. He had several choices of design. He could choose to have round or straight sails. He could have red, blue, green or yellow sails. He could have a flag at the top of the mainmast. He could have a curved or a pointed hull (you may need to explain that this is the part that sits in the water). He also had a choice of red, blue, green or yellow for the hull.

- You may wish to ask the students to pick a design and sketch one on the board or on an OHT. Or you may have acetates already drawn to demonstrate different yachts.

- Ask them to sketch a yacht in their books, using the above choices.

- Now ask the students to hold up their sketches if they include a flag.

- Repeat this for, say, a blue sail, a red hull, a blue sail and a red hull, a green sail with a flag and a pointed hull.

- The students should now understand the words associated with the parts of a yacht and be able also to pick out relevant information as requested.

- You could, with the help of students, now record parts of the data for the class by yacht type in a two-way table on the board. For example:

	Round sails	Straight sails
Blue	6	4
Red	3	7
Green	2	4
Yellow	5	1

- You could also compare the boys' results with the girls' results.

- Now ask the class to look at the pictures of the yachts in Pupil Book 1. Ask them to describe in words one of the yachts. For example:'It has round blue sails with a flag at the top of the mainmast and a curved red hull.'

- **The class can now do Exercise 3D from Pupil Book 1.**

1 **a** 10 **b** 7 **c** 2 **d** 8 **e** 10 **f** 4 **g** 3 **h** 3 **i** 4 **j** 2
2 **a** $\frac{1}{2}$ **b** $\frac{7}{20}$ **c** $\frac{1}{10}$ **d** $\frac{2}{5}$ **e** $\frac{1}{2}$ **f** $\frac{1}{5}$ **g** $\frac{3}{20}$ **h** $\frac{3}{20}$ **i** $\frac{1}{5}$ **j** $\frac{1}{10}$
3 **a** Yes **b** Yes **c** No **d** Yes **e** Yes **f** Yes **g** No **h** Yes **i** Yes **j** No
  k Yes **l** Yes **m** Yes (but not in the 20 yachts in the above questions) **n** Yes
  o No **p** No

Plenary

- Sum up the lesson by asking the class which yachts they think are the most popular types from the 20 in Exercise 3D.
- Ask them how they decided.
- Explain to the students that the homework is to use the information provided about the yachts to find out whether their answers to Exercise 3D were correct.
- Point out that if two things are the most popular, you can have either.

Key Words

- events
- probability
- dice
- chance
- information

Homework

1 The table gives the data about each yacht type.

Yacht	Round sails/ straight sails	Colour of sails	Flag/ no flag	Curved hull/ Pointed hull	Colour of hull
1	Round	Blue	Yes	Curved	Red
2	Straight	Red	No	Pointed	Red
3	Straight	Green	Yes	Pointed	Blue
4	Round	Yellow	No	Curved	Blue
5	Straight	Blue	Yes	Curved	Yellow
6	Round	Yellow	Yes	Pointed	Green
7	Straight	Red	No	Curved	Blue
8	Round	Blue	Yes	Pointed	Red
9	Round	Green	No	Curved	Yellow
10	Straight	Blue	No	Pointed	Red
11	Round	Red	No	Pointed	Blue
12	Straight	Red	Yes	Curved	Blue
13	Straight	Green	No	Curved	Yellow
14	Straight	Blue	No	Curved	Red
15	Round	Red	No	Pointed	Blue
16	Round	Blue	No	Pointed	Yellow
17	Round	Red	Yes	Curved	Red
18	Straight	Green	Yes	Pointed	Blue
19	Round	Blue	No	Pointed	Red
20	Straight	Red	No	Curved	Red

Work out the most popular choice of each category and find out whether there is a yacht of that type in the list. If two categories are equal, you can choose either.

Homework Answers

1 The most popular feature in each case is: round sail or straight sail(10 each); blue or red sails (7 each); no flag; pointed or curved (10 each) red hull
  The yachts that are most popular must have no flag, with a red or blue sail and a red hull. They are numbers 2, 10 14, 19

Framework objectives – Experimental probability

Estimate probabilities from experimental data; understand that:
  if an experiment is repeated there may be, and usually will be, different outcomes;
  increasing the number of times an experiment is repeated generally leads to better estimates of probability.

Oral and mental starter

- Use a multiplication table or write the first five rows on the board or OHT.

1	2	3	4	5	6	7	8	9	10
2	4	6	8	10	12	*14*	16	18	20
3	6	9	12	15	18	*21*	24	27	30
4	8	12	16	20	24	28	32	36	40
5	10	15	20	25	30	35	40	45	50

- Ask a student to pick two numbers from the same column. For example:
      14 and 21, as shown in italic.
- Now ask the class to say them as a fraction (fourteen twenty-firsts).
- Now tell the class to look at the beginning of the two rows chosen and say what fraction they see (two-thirds).
- Ask them if they can tell you anything about the fractions formed by the numbers in each column of the table. (They are equivalent.)
- Point out that this always works, for example $\frac{9}{36} = \frac{1}{4}$.
- Now pick out your own fractions and ask them to give you an equivalent fraction.
- You could then work this backwards by giving them a fraction in its simplest form and asking for an equivalent fraction. You could say: 'I want $\frac{3}{4}$ changed into sixteenths.'

Main lesson activity

- Explain to the class that you want to be able to predict whether, for example, the next person who comes through the door watches 'Eastenders'. Ask how they would collect the information needed.
- Note on the board any key words that are given. For example: tally, observation sheet, survey, sample.
- Conduct a survey of the class by recording data about their hair colour.
- Now use the result to obtain the experimental probability. Allow the class time to put this information into their books.
- Ask them, in pairs or groups, to make a list of the types of information that they could collect to estimates probabilities. You may need to prompt them with a few examples, such as the number of times a six is thrown to test the fairness of a dice, the number of times the school bus was late this month, the sex of shoppers at a supermarket.

- **The class can now do Exercise 3E from Pupil Book 1.**

Plenary

- Tell the class that when a fair, standard dice is rolled, the probability of getting any one of the six scores is $\frac{1}{6}$. Ask why they would be unlikely to get $\frac{1}{6}$ if the scores from six throws of the dice are recorded and probability is calculated from their results.
- Remind them that experiments are prone to errors, but the more trials carried out, the more reliable the results tend to be.

Key Words

- data
- experimental probability
- different outcomes
- estimate of probability

Homework

This homework is connected to the extension work, which some students may already have started.

1 Having decided on an experiment of your own, collect your data. Try to collect as much as possible.

2 Write a brief report about the data you have collected.

3 Work out an experimental probability for your data.

Number 2

Framework objectives – Fractions and decimals
Use division to convert a fraction to a decimal.
Simplify fractions by cancelling all common factors. *(Year 7 objective.)*

Oral and mental starter

- This is an exercise in adding and subtracting integers.
- Using a target board, such as the one shown, explain that the object is to add the first three values in a column and then subtract the final value.
- Ask an individual student to do this or ask the class to note totals on a piece of paper. (Totals here are 18, 20, 15, 30.)
- This can be repeated for the rows by adding the first three and subtracting the last one. (Totals here are 11, 17, 5, 10.)
- To make the activity easier, the bottom row can be covered and the first two numbers in each column added, and then the third number subtracted. (Totals are 19, 3, 25, 24.)
- Similarly, the last column can be covered.

	12	10	7	18
+	8	6	20	17
+	1	13	2	11
−	3	9	14	16
	+	+	−	

Main lesson activity

- The students have already met simple cancelling in Pupil Book 1 of Year 7. However, they will need to be reminded of the process.
- Ask them for a fraction equivalent to $\frac{15}{20}$. Make sure the process of cancelling, in this case by 5 (the HCF), is understood, namely: $\frac{15}{20} = \frac{3}{4}$.
- Repeat with other fractions. For example: $\frac{9}{12} (= \frac{3}{4})$, $\frac{20}{25} (= \frac{4}{5})$, $\frac{12}{20} (= \frac{3}{5})$, $\frac{45}{100} (= \frac{9}{20})$.
- Ask the students for any equivalent fractions, decimals and percentages they know.
- They are likely to come up with at least $\frac{1}{2} = 0.5 = 50\%$, $\frac{1}{4} = 0.25 = 25\%$ and $\frac{3}{4} = 0.75 = 75\%$.
- If not already mentioned, ask them what fraction is equivalent to 0.6.
- Discuss the place value of 0.6 and explain that it can be written as $\frac{6}{10}$, which cancels to $\frac{3}{5}$.
- Repeat with 0.4 $(= \frac{4}{10} = \frac{2}{5})$ and 0.88 $(= \frac{88}{100} = \frac{22}{25})$.
- And again with 0.7 $(= \frac{7}{10})$ and 0.35 $(= \frac{7}{20})$.
- Move onto the conversion of fractions to decimals. For example: $\frac{2}{5} = \frac{4}{10} = 0.4$ and $\frac{9}{25} = \frac{36}{100} = 0.36$.

- **The class can now do Exercise 4A from Pupil Book 1.**

1 a $\frac{1}{3}$ b $\frac{2}{3}$ c $\frac{2}{3}$ d $\frac{3}{4}$ e $\frac{9}{10}$ f $\frac{2}{5}$ g $\frac{1}{3}$ h $\frac{1}{2}$ i $\frac{1}{6}$ j $\frac{3}{5}$ k $\frac{2}{3}$ l $\frac{5}{7}$

2 a $\frac{1}{5}$ b $\frac{2}{5}$ c $\frac{1}{10}$ d $\frac{3}{10}$ e $\frac{3}{5}$ f $\frac{9}{10}$ g $\frac{1}{2}$ h $\frac{4}{5}$

3 a $\frac{1}{4}$ b $\frac{9}{20}$ c $\frac{3}{25}$ d $\frac{19}{50}$ e $\frac{33}{50}$ f $\frac{19}{20}$ g $\frac{13}{25}$ h $\frac{21}{25}$ i $\frac{7}{25}$ j $\frac{13}{20}$ k $\frac{49}{50}$ l $\frac{9}{25}$ m $\frac{1}{20}$

 n $\frac{3}{50}$ o $\frac{12}{25}$ p $\frac{3}{20}$

4 a 0.6 b 0.15 c 0.12 d 0.06

5 a 0.5 b 0.25 c 0.2 d 0.1 e 0.05 f 0.04 g 0.02 h 0.01

Extension 4A Answers

The ninths recur in a form similar to the 'eleven times table', that is: 0.1111, 0.2222, 0.3333, etc.

Plenary

- Write a lot of fractions on the board in random order, such as $\frac{8}{20}$, $\frac{2}{10}$, $\frac{5}{15}$, $\frac{5}{25}$, $\frac{3}{9}$, $\frac{3}{15}$, $\frac{2}{11}$, $\frac{14}{100}$, $\frac{9}{21}$.
- Ask the students to cancel down each of the fractions.
- Ask them to explain which fractions can be written easily as decimals and why (denominators of 10 and 100).

Key Words

- numerator
- denominator
- terminating decimal
- recurring decimal
- simplest form

Homework

1 Write each of the following decimals as a fraction with a denominator of 10 or 100. Then cancel to its simplest form if possible.

 a 0.4 b 0.32 c 0.62 d 0.7

2 Write down each of the following as a terminating decimal.

 a $\frac{7}{20}$ b $\frac{3}{4}$ c $\frac{4}{5}$ d $\frac{11}{50}$ e $\frac{9}{10}$

Answers

1 a $\frac{2}{5}$ b $\frac{8}{25}$ c $\frac{31}{50}$ d $\frac{7}{10}$

2 a 0.35 b 0.75 c 0.8 d 0.22 e 0.9

LESSON 4.2

Framework objectives – Adding and subtracting fractions

Add and subtract fractions with a common denominator. Calculate fractions of quantities (fraction answers). Multiply and divide an integer by a fraction.

Oral and mental starter

- Use a number line drawn on board, or a counting stick. Mark or state that one end is 0 and the other end is 1, as shown.

0   1

- Ask the students to identify the rest of the marks on the stick.
- As a group, or with an individual student, count in units of 0.1.
- The students can have the positions pointed out to them on the line or stick until the end is reached, when they have to continue without prompts.
- Repeat, possibly with different individuals, to establish a class 'record'.
- Repeat the activity with the line or stick marked with 0 and 2, as shown.

0   2

- Alternatively, count down from 1 or 2 to 0.

Main lesson activity

- Write on the board: $\frac{1}{5} + \frac{3}{5}$.
- Ask the class for the answer. Many students may give $\frac{4}{10}$.
- Get the correct answer and discuss the process used to add fractions with the same denominator.
- The students have met this before and should recall the need to leave the denominator unchanged.
- Repeat with $\frac{5}{12} + \frac{1}{12} = \frac{6}{12}$, and $\frac{7}{10} + \frac{5}{10} = \frac{12}{10} = 1\frac{2}{10} = 1\frac{1}{5}$.
- Recall the need to write top-heavy fractions as mixed numbers, and to cancel down where possible.
- Now ask for the answer to $\frac{7}{10} - \frac{2}{10} = \frac{5}{10} = \frac{1}{2}$.
- The method is basically the same, but with the top two numbers subtracted instead of added.
- Repeat with $\frac{4}{5} - \frac{1}{5} = \frac{3}{5}$, and $\frac{7}{15} - \frac{4}{15} = \frac{3}{15} = \frac{1}{5}$.
- Now ask for the answer to $\frac{4}{5}$ of 45.
- Recall the method to do this: find $\frac{1}{5}$ of 45 (= 9) and then multiply by 4 (= 36).
- Repeat with $\frac{3}{4}$ of £28 (= £21), $\frac{2}{7}$ of 35 kg (= 10 kg).
- Finally, ask for the answers to $3 \times \frac{4}{7}$ (= $\frac{12}{7}$ = $1\frac{5}{7}$) and $5 \times \frac{4}{5}$ (= $\frac{20}{5}$ = 4).

- **The class can now do Exercise 4B from Pupil Book 1.**

38   © HarperCollins*Publishers* Ltd 2003

Plenary

- Draw a 2 × 3 grid on the board.
- Discuss how this can be used to add $\frac{1}{2} + \frac{1}{3} (= \frac{5}{6})$.
- Repeat with a 4 × 3 grid and $\frac{1}{6} + \frac{3}{4} (= \frac{11}{12})$.
- Repeat with a 4 × 6 grid and $\frac{1}{3} + \frac{3}{8} (= \frac{17}{24})$.

Key Words

☐ denominator
☐ top-heavy fraction
☐ mixed number

Homework

1 Work out each of the following, cancelling down or writing as a mixed number as appropriate.

  a $\frac{1}{7} + \frac{2}{7}$ b $\frac{5}{8} + \frac{7}{8}$ c $\frac{7}{10} + \frac{1}{10}$ d $\frac{1}{5} + \frac{2}{5} + \frac{3}{5}$
  e $\frac{2}{7} - \frac{1}{7}$ f $\frac{5}{8} - \frac{1}{8}$ g $\frac{7}{10} - \frac{1}{10}$ h $\frac{3}{5} + \frac{2}{5} - \frac{1}{5}$

2 Work out each of these.

  a $\frac{4}{9}$ of £36   b $\frac{3}{7}$ of 49 kg

3 Work out each of these, cancelling down or writing as mixed numbers as appropriate.

  a $3 \times \frac{5}{9}$ b $4 \times \frac{3}{8}$

Answers
  1 a $\frac{3}{7}$ b $1\frac{1}{2}$ c $\frac{4}{5}$ d $1\frac{1}{5}$ e $\frac{1}{7}$ f $\frac{1}{2}$ g $\frac{3}{5}$ h $\frac{4}{5}$
  2 a £16 b 21 kg
  3 a $1\frac{2}{3}$ b $1\frac{1}{2}$

LESSON 4.3

Framework objectives – Percentages

Interpret percentage as the operator 'so many hundredths of' and express one given number as a percentage of another.

Oral and mental starter

- Ask the students to think of products that make 100 (for example, 1×100, 2×50, 4×25, 5×20, 10×10).
- Now use a target board like the one shown, and ask the students to give the percentage equivalent to each fraction.
- Discuss how to do this: multiply the denominator by a number to make 100, and then multiply the numerator by the same number.
- Answers for the grid are shown below.

$\frac{1}{2}$	$\frac{3}{10}$	$\frac{7}{20}$	$\frac{2}{5}$
$\frac{11}{20}$	$\frac{7}{10}$	$\frac{43}{50}$	$\frac{3}{5}$
$\frac{1}{5}$	$\frac{1}{4}$	$\frac{1}{20}$	$\frac{12}{25}$
$\frac{9}{25}$	$\frac{9}{50}$	$\frac{4}{5}$	$\frac{3}{4}$

50%	30%	35%	40%
55%	70%	86%	60%
20%	25%	5%	48%
36%	18%	80%	75%

Main lesson activity

- This follows on from the oral and mental starter.
- Ask the students 'What percentage of 50 is 32?'
- Discuss ways of doing this without a calculator.
- Establish the fraction $\frac{32}{50}$ and multiply top and bottom by 2 to get $\frac{64}{100}$, which is 64%.
- Also write on the board that 32 out of 50 is the same as 64 out of 100.
- Repeat the process with 15 out of 20 (75%) and 3 out of 10 (30%).
- Now ask the students how they would compare two sets of exam marks, such as 19 out of 25 and 16 out of 20.
- Converting each to a percentage gives 76% and 80%. So 16 out of 20 is the better mark.

- **The class can now do Exercise 4C from Pupil Book 1.**

Plenary

- Write four values on the left-hand side of board, such as 5, 12, 15 and 40.
- Write the following values on the right-hand side of board: 10, 20, 25 and 50.
- Make four pairs of values, each pair consisting of a left-hand value and a right-hand value.
- Calculate for each pair the left-hand value as a percentage of the right-hand value.

Key Words

- equivalent
- fraction
- denominator
- rounding off

Homework

1 Without using a calculator, work out what percentage the first value is of the second value.

a 45 out of 50	**b** 13 out of 20	**c** 22 out of 25	**d** 16 out of 20
e 21 out of 50	**f** 28 out of 100	**g** 15 out of 25	**h** 4 out of 20

2 In the Year 10 exams, Tamsin scored 84 out of 100 in Maths, 44 out of 50 in English and 21 out of 25 in Science. Convert these scores into a percentage. In which test did Tamsin do best?

Answers
 1 a 90% **b** 65% **c** 88% **d** 80% **e** 42% **f** 28% **g** 60% **h** 20%
 2 Maths 84%, English 88%, Science 84%; Tamsin did best in English.

LESSON 4.4

Framework objectives – Percentage increase and decrease

Calculate percentages and find the outcome of a given percentage increase or decrease.

Oral and mental starter

- Use a target board, such as the one shown on the right
- Recall the mental method for multiplying a two-digit number by a single-digit number (partitioning). For example: $7 \times 23 = 7 \times 20 + 7 \times 3 = 140 + 21 = 161$.
- Roll a dice (preferably a ten-sided dice). Ask the students to multiply, in turn, the numbers on the target board by the score on the dice.
- Do this with individual students or ask the class to write down the answers. (Some jotting could be allowed.)

28	38	17	22	60
18	16	14	26	48
30	52	36	19	13
32	15	12	24	34

Main lesson activity

- Ask the students what they understand by percentage increase and decrease.
- Ask them where these occur in everyday life (for example, sales, pay rises).
- Give an example. A cooker is reduced by 10% in a sale. If its original price was £320, what is its sale price? (The students may need to be introduced to the vocabulary of cost price, sale price, selling price, etc.)
- Work through the example. First, calculate 10% of £320 (£32). Then deduct this from the original price, £320 – £32 = £288.
- Give another example. A person earning £250 per week is given a 20% pay rise. What is her new weekly pay? (£300).
- If necessary, do more examples, but keep the increase/decrease to simple percentages, such as 5%, 10%, 20%, etc.

- **The class can now do Exercise 4D from Pupil Book 1.**

Plenary

- Put on the board several percentages, such as 5%, 10%, 20%, 25%, and a variety of quantities, such as £32, 58 kg, 200 km and £150.
- Apply each percentage value to each quantity and calculate a percentage increase or decrease, as appropriate.

Key Words

- percentage
- increase/decrease
- reduction
- value added tax (VAT)
- sale price
- original price
- selling price

Homework

Do not use a calculator.

1 A car has a top speed of 130 miles per hour. After tuning, the top speed increases by 10%.

   a How many miles per hour faster is the car now?

   b What is the new top speed of the car?

2 Work out the final amount when:

   a £40 is increased by 20%   **b** £60 is decreased by 10%

   c £140 is increased by 25%   **d** £80 is decreased by 20%

Answers
   1 a 13 mph   **b** 143 mph
   2 a £48   **b** £54   **c** £175   **d** £64

Framework objectives – Real-life problems

Recall known facts, including fraction to decimal conversions. Use known facts to derive unknown facts, including products such as 0.7 and 6, and 0.03 and 8.

Oral and mental starter

- Recall methods of multiplying integers and decimals expressed to one decimal place: for example, $7 \times 0.8 = 5.6$.
- Use this to ask for answers to a variety of similar questions.
- As these can be hard to verbalise and for students to conceptualise, a grid, as shown, could be used.
- Particular squares could be pointed at and individual students asked for the product.

×	0.8	0.3	0.2	0.6
7				
5				
2				
3				

Main lesson activity

- This is a lesson on practical situations in which percentages are used.
- Introduce with the real-life situation of buying goods on credit.
- Ask the students what they know about buying goods on credit.
- Establish that usually a deposit is required, followed by so many monthly payments. For example, a bike which normally sells for £300 can be bought for a 20% deposit followed by 12 monthly payments of £25. How much will it cost buying by credit? What percentage of the original cost is the extra cost?

  Deposit = 20% of £300 = £60
  Monthly payments = 12 × £25 = £300
  Total = £60 + £300 = £360
  Extra cost = £360 – £300 = £60
  £60 as percentage of £300 is the same as £20 out of £100: that is 20%.
- The students will find some of these concepts difficult. Other examples may be needed and/or help given with the exercise.
- Calculators will be needed.

- **The class can now do Exercise 4E from Pupil Book 1.**

Plenary

- Go over the problems that students encountered in doing the exercise, together with any other difficulties that they have in working with percentages.
- If time permits, discuss some of the aspects of percentages in real life. For example, National Insurance, with tax bands, higher-rate tax, credit, hire purchase and bank loans.

Key Words

- deposit
- percentage profit
- percentage loss
- credit
- cost price
- selling price

Homework

1 A scooter that normally costs £1600 can be bought using two different payment plans.

Plan	Deposit	Number of payments	Each payment
A	20%	24	£65
B	50%	12	£70

a Work out how much the scooter costs using each plan.

b Work out the percentage of the original price that each plan costs.

2 A shop buys a table for £50 and sells it for £80. Work out the percentage profit made by the shop.

Answers
1 Plan A: **a** £1880   **b** 117.5%
  Plan B: **a** £1640   **b** 102.5%
2 60%

Algebra 2

Framework objectives – Algebraic shorthand
Know that algebraic operations follow the same conventions and order as arithmetic operations.
Begin to distinguish the different roles played by letter symbols in equations.

Oral and mental starter

- Ask the class to count down from 10 to zero.
- Now ask them to count down from 10, but in steps of a half: ten, nine and a half, nine, eight and a half, … zero.
- Now ask for a countdown from ten in steps of 0.5:
  10, 9.5, 9.0, 8.5, … zero.
- Now ask for a countdown from ten in steps of 0.2:
  10, 9.8, 9.6, 9.4, 9.2, 9.0, 8.8, … zero.
- Now ask for a countdown from ten in steps of 0.4:
  10, 9.6, 9.2, 8.8, … zero.
- If this is proving difficult mentally then try putting the numbers on the board as the students respond.
- This can be extended if needed into steps of 0.3, or even $1\frac{1}{2}$.

Main lesson activity

- Remind the class of the meaning of the words **term** and **expression**. A term is an algebraic quantity which contains only a letter (or combination of letters) and may contain a number. An expression is a combination of signs, often with numbers.
- Next, show them, with examples of terms such as $8m$ for $8 \times m$ and $5cd$ for $5 \times c \times d$, that the multiplication symbol is omitted whenever this is possible. Ask the students if they know the reason for this. (Because the symbol is easily confused with x, which is much used in algebra.)
- Go on to show that the use of the divide symbol is also avoided whenever possible. For example,

  $\dfrac{10}{q}$ is written instead of $p \div q$.

- Stress the convention of always placing the coefficient on the left of the letters, such as in $5 \times m = 5m$, $c \times 6d = 6cd$.

- **Get the class to answer Question 1, Exercise 5A from Pupil Book 8.1.**

- Then talk about the = sign, and explain that it means 'has the same value as' and not 'exactly the same form as'. For example, in $3 + 4 = 4 + 3$, each side has the same value, but not exactly the same form, as one side is written in the opposite order to the other.
- Explain that algebra can be used to identify useful patterns and properties in operations in arithmetic. For example, $a + b = b + a$ illustrates that two numbers can always be added the other way round to get the same answer.
- Ask the class if the same thing will work for subtraction. Is $a - b = b - a$? You will need to demonstrate that they are not the same with an example such as $5 - 1$. Is it the same as $1 - 5$? The first equals 4, the other –4, so they are not the same.
- Ask if it works for multiplication. Is $ab = ba$? You will need to show a few examples before everyone is convinced: For example, $3 \times 4 = 4 \times 3$.

- Ask if division will work the same way. Again, show some examples that it does not work.

- **The class can now do Exercise 5A, Questions 2 to 5 from Pupil Book 1.**

- Explain to the class that it is very easy to misuse the equals sign, and this must be avoided. Lead them through the solving of the equation $x + 2 = 23$.
- With $x + 2 = 23$ on the board, ask the class what has to be added to 2 to give 23.
- This gives $x = 21$. Show on the board how to write the solution with one equals sign under the other.

- **The class can now do the rest of Exercise 5A from Pupil Book 1.**

Exercise 5A Answers

1 **a** $3n$ **b** $5n$ **c** $7m$ **d** $8t$ **e** ab **f** mn **g** $5p$ **h** $4q$ **i** $\frac{m}{3}$ **j** $\frac{5}{n}$ **k** $7w$
 l kd **m** $3t$ **n** $\frac{8}{k}$ **p** $9m$ **q** gh
2 **a** 6 **b** 3 **c** m **d** 4 **e** 8 **f** h **g** 7 **h** 4 **i** y **j** 1 **k** 7 **l** w
 m it doesn't matter which way round you have the question
3 **a** 2 **b** 5 **c** n **d** 6 **e** 7 **f** k **g** 7 **h** 6 **i** x **j** 6 **k** 8 **l** w
 m it doesn't matter which way round you have the question
4 **a** 3, –3 **b** 5, –5 **c** 8, –8 **d** the two values must be the same
 b any more pairs, which are the same **b** $m = t$
5 **a** p **b** t **c** q, r **d** kg **e** a **f** p **g** tf **h** $p \times t$
6 **a** 10 **b** 8 **c** 15 **d** 14 **e** 6 **f** 15 **g** 5 **h** 15 **i** 45 **j** 77 **k** 65 **l** 72
7 **a** $2 \times 7 = 7 \times 2$ **b** $m \times n = mn$ **c** $p \times q = qp$ **d** $2 \div 4 = \frac{2}{4}$ **e** $a \div b, \frac{a}{b}$
 f $4 \times 19 = 19 \times 4$ **g** $6 + x = x + 6$ **h** $3y = 3 \times y$

Extension Answers

The true statements are 1, 2 and 5.

Plenary

Key Words

- Go through the shorthand routines of algebra, asking the students why they are useful. Also discuss the use and misuse of the equals sign.
- Revisit the solution of simple equations, such as $x + 3 = 18$.

symbol
term
expression
equals

Homework

1 Write each of these expressions in the simplest way.

 a $5 \times p$ **b** $2 \times t$ **c** $8 \times q$ **d** $k \times t$ **e** $m \div 3$ **f** $5 \div n$

 g $m \div k$ **h** $m \times n \times p$

2 Solve each of the following equations, making correct use of the equals sign.

 a $x + 1 = 21$ **b** $x - 3 = 18$ **c** $x + 4 = 29$ **d** $x + 1 = 13$

 e $x - 8 = 17$ **f** $x + 3 = 11$ **g** $x + 9 = 12$ **h** $x - 7 = 10$

Answers
 1 **a** $5p$ **b** $2t$ **c** $8q$ **d** kt **e** $\frac{m}{3}$ **f** $\frac{5}{n}$ **g** $\frac{m}{k}$ **h** mnp
 2 **a** $x = 20$ **b** $x = 21$ **c** $x = 25$ **d** $x = 12$ **e** $x = 25$ **f** $x = 8$ **g** $x = 3$ **h** $x = 17$

Framework objectives – Two rules of algebra

Simplify linear expressions by collecting like terms.

Use index notation for small positive integer powers.

Oral and mental starter

- You are going to ask the class for a number and give them a number back. They have to guess the rule.
- Start with the rule 'double and add 1'.
- Ask the students in turn for a number. Say it is 7. Reply after you have applied the rule, which here will give 15.
- Who will be first to guess the rule?
- Use other rules such as 'Take away from 50', 'add 3 and double'.
- Invite some students to think of a rule and get other students to give them numbers.
- This can develop into a team game, one half of the class versus the other half, taking it in turns to think of the rule and then to guess. The number of guesses could be limited to so many turns, or a score kept of how many guesses had to be made, or how many numbers had to be processed.
- Nothing is to be written down – it's all mental arithmetic!

Main lesson activity

- Put on the board the sum $3 + 3 + 3 + 3$. Ask the class whether there is another way of writing this sum. The two answers you want are: 4×3 (because there are four threes) and 12.
- Go through a few more on the board such as $5 + 5 + 5 = 5 \times 3 = 15$.
- Now put on the board $m + m + m + m$, and ask the class for another way of writing this. The two answers you want are: $4 \times m$ and the shorthand $4m$.

- **The class can now do Questions 1 and 2, Exercise 5B from Pupil Book 1.**

- Now talk about multiplying letters together.
- Put on the board $m \times m \times m$. Ask the class why this in *not* $3m$. Try with an example if they do not see why. Use $m = 2$, then $m \times m \times m = 8$ and $3m = 3 \times 2 = 6$.

- **The class can now do the rest of Exercise 5B from Pupil Book 1.**

- Tell the class that a short way of writing, for example, $2 \times 2 \times 2$ is 2^3. Explain that the small number at the top right is called a *power* or *index*. It tells us how many times to multiply a number by itself. So, for example, $m \times m \times m \times m = m^4$. That is m to the power of four.

1 **a** $2m$ **b** $3k$ **c** $4a$ **d** $3d$ **e** $4q$ **f** $2t$ **g** $4n$ **h** $3g$ **i** $3p$ **j** $4w$ **k** $5i$
   l $4a$
2 **a** $3p$ **b** $4m$ **c** $3 \times k = 3k$ **d** $5 \times h = 5h$ **e** $m + m + m + m + m + m$
   f $p + p + p + p + p = 5p$ **g** $g + g + g = 3g$ **h** $n + n + n + n + n + n + n = 7 \times n$
   i $y + y + y + y + y = 5 \times y$
3 **a** n^3 **b** m^2 **c** p^4 **d** w^3 **e** m^3 **f** t^4 **g** k^4 **h** y^3 **i** v^4 **j** d^5 **k** t^5 **l** m^3
4 **a** 27 **b** 16 **c** 16 **d** 64 **e** 125 **f** 8 **g** 81 **h** 100 **i** 1000 **j** 32
5 **a** n^2 **b** $2m$ **c** p^3 **d** $3w$ **e** q^4 **f** $4r$ **g** $2k$ **h** f^3 **i** $4v$ **j** d^5 **k** $3q$
   l t^4
6 **a** $t + t + t, t \times t \times t$ **b** $m + m + m + m, m \times m \times m \times m$ **c** $k + k, k \times k$
   d $w + w + w + w + w, w \times w \times w \times w \times w, d + d + d, d \times d \times d$

Plenary

- Ask the class how we know that $3t$ is different from t^3.
- Substitute any value into both expressions, which shows immediately that we shall see that they are different. For example, use $t = 2$.
- Then $3t = 3 \times 2 = 6$ and $t^3 = 2 \times 2 \times 2 = 8$.

Key Words

- index
- power

Homework

1 Copy and complete each of the following.

   a $p + p = 2 \times p = \square$ **b** $t + t + t = 3 \times t = \square$

   c $d + d + d + d + d = \square \times d = \square$ **d** $n + n + n + n = \square = \square$

   e $i + i + i + i + i + i = \square = \square$ **f** $\square = 5 \times q = 5q$

   g $\square = 4 \times m = \square$ **h** $\square = 4 \times k = \square$

   i $\square = \square = 5p$ **j** $\square = \square = 6a$

2 Write each of the following expressions as a power.

   a $p \times p \times p \times p$ **b** $n \times n \times n$ **c** $i \times i \times i \times i \times i$ **d** $q \times q \times q$

   e $t + t + t + t + t$ **f** $w + w + w + w$ **g** $d \times d \times d \times d$ **h** $p \times p \times p$

   i $u \times u \times u \times u \times u$ **j** $m + m + m$ **k** $h \times h \times h \times h$ **l** $p + p + p$

Answers

1 **a** $2p$ **b** $3t$ **c** $5 \times d = 5d$ **d** $4 \times n = 4n$ **e** $6 \times i = 6i$ **f** $q + q + q + q + q$ **g** $m + m + m + m = 4m$
   h $k + k + k + k = 4k$ **i** $p + p + p + p + p = 5 \times p$ **j** $a + a + a + a + a + a = 6 \times a$
2 **a** p^4 **b** n^3 **c** i^5 **d** q^3 **e** $5t$ **f** $4w$ **g** d^4 **h** p^3 **i** u^5 **j** $3m$ **k** h^4 **l** $3p$

Framework Objectives – Like terms and simplification

Simplify linear expressions by collecting like terms.

Oral and mental starter

- Ask the class what the **approximate** answer is to 314×8.
- Put the suggested answers on the board, but do not accept any calculated answers. (The correct answer is 2512).
- Talk about the guesses (which may be more than two significant figures). Explain that these are not approximations.
- Show how to estimate by rounding off the numbers to the nearest convenient values, and then multiplying. For example:

    314 is rounded off to $300 \times 8 = 2400$.
- Ask the class whether this estimate is known to be too high or too low.
- It is of course too low, because 314 has been rounded down and the 8 has not been changed.
- Now estimate 298×8.
- This time 298 is rounded up, so the estimate is going to be high at $300 \times 8 = 2400$.
- Continue with more approximations, asking the students whether each is too high or too low. For example:

    417×4 (1600 – low) 579×4 (2400 – high) 823×5 (4000 – low)
    686×6 (4200 – high) 309×5 (1500 – low) 793×7 (5600 – high).

Main lesson activity

- Say to the class: 'If you own three cups and buy another five cups, how many cups do you have altogether?'.
- State that in algebra this situation can be represented by: $3c + 5c = 8c$, and write this expression on the board.
- Explain that the terms here are called **like terms**, because they are all multiples of c.
- Next, put on the board $n + n + n + n + n$. Ask the class for the simplest way of writing this. It is $5n$. Emphasise the convention of always placing the **coefficient** on the left of the letter.
- Then put on the board $3n + 2n + 4n$. What is the simple way of writing this? It is $9n$. You will have to show that three ns are added to two ns and the result is added to four ns to give nine ns.
- Emphasise that these terms in n are like terms. Ask the class for examples of other like terms.
- Put on the board $3x^2$, and ask the class for like terms ($2x^2$, $7x^2$, etc).
- Explain that only like terms can be added or subtracted to simplify an expression. For example: $5m + 6m$ gives $11m$, $7g - 2g$ gives $5g$. But **unlike terms**, such as $2m + 3g$, cannot be combined.
- Show a few more examples of like terms being combined.

- **The class can now do Questions 1 to 3, Exercise 5C from Pupil Book 1.**

- Now put on the board $3a + 2b + 4a$. Ask the class if this expression can be simplified at all.
- Lead the class to suggest adding the like terms to get $7a + 2b$.
- You may well need to again demonstrate that $9ab$ is the wrong answer.
- Go through more examples, such as $2t + 5k + t$, which gives $(3t + 5k)$. Try some more complex expressions, such as $2xy + 7xy + 3pq$ $(9xy + 3pq)$ and $6x^2 + 3y^2 + x^2$ $(9x^2 + 3y^2)$.
- Also go through examples involving subtraction, such as $5m + 4d - 2m$, which gives $3m + 4d$. Again, try some more complex expressions, such as $3xy + 5xy - 6xy$ $(2xy)$ and $7x^2 + 2y - 6z + 2x^2 - 3y$ $(9x^2 - y - 6z)$.

- **The class can now complete Exercise 5C from Pupil Book 1.**

1 a $5b$ **b** $7x$ **c** $7m$ **d** $6m$ **e** $4d$ **f** $5g$ **g** $3k$ **h** $4t$
2 a $4g$ **b** $2x$ **c** $2h$ **d** $8q$ **e** $7h$ **f** $5x$ **g** $6y$ **h** $7d$ **i** $3x$ **j** $2m$ **k** $3k$
 l $2n$
3 a $3t, 5t, 9t$ and $g, 8g, 7g$ **b** $m, 4m, 10m$ and $7p, 9p, 3p$
  c $4k, k$ and $3m, 8m, 7m$ and $5w, 7w$ **d** $x^2, 5x^2, 3x^2$ and $t, 3t, 4t$
  e $y^2, 7y^2, 4y^2$ and $2y, 8y, 3y$ **f** $7w, 4w, 3w$ and $7g, 3g, 10g$ and $3h, 9h$
4 a $5b + 5$ **b** $5x + 7$ **c** $6m + 2$ **d** $7k + 8$ **e** $2x + 7$ **f** $3k + 4$ **g** $4p + 3$
  h $d + 1$ **i** $3m - 3$ **j** $4t - 4$ **k** $w - 8$ **l** $4g - 1$ **m** $5t + k$ **n** $7x + 2y$
  p $7k + 3g$ **q** $3h + 3w$ **r** $2t - 2p$ **s** $n - 2t$ **t** $p + 2q$ **u** $2p$
5 a $7t + 5g$ **b** $6x + 4y$ **c** $5m + 3k$ **d** $3x + 4y$ **e** $2m + 5p$ **f** $2n + 7t$
  g $4k + 2g$ **h** $2d + b$ **i** $q + 2p$ **j** $6g - 4k$ **k** $7x - 5y$ **l** $d - 5e$
6 a $6x^2$ **b** $8k^2$ **c** $7m^2$ **d** $4d^2$ **e** $2g^2$ **f** $2a^2$ **g** $7f^2$ **h** $2y^2$ **i** $4t^2$ **j** $3h^2$
  k $7k^2$ **l** $4m^2$
7 a $10x + 8$ **b** $6p + 5k$ **c** $11t + 4m$ **d** $4k + 5t$ **e** $2m + 5p$ **f** $6w + 5d$
  g $8x + 6y$ **h** $5p + 7q$ **i** $2m + 5t$

Plenary

- Ask the class what like terms are. Can they be added or subtracted to simplify an expression?
- Call for some examples of like terms being combined.
- Move onto unlike terms and the fact that they cannot be combined. Again call for examples.
- Go through any wrong answers to the questions in Exercise 5C to ensure that all the students concerned are now able to cope with the arithmetic of terms.

Key Words

- simplify
- coefficient
- like terms
- unlike terms

Homework

1 From each cloud, group together the like terms

a

$3p$ $6g$ p
$4g$ g $5p$
$8p$ $7g$

b

$3q$ $4m$ q
m $2m$ $9q$
$5m$

c

$4x^2$ $2y$
$4t$ x^2
$8y$ $9t$

2 Simplify each of the following expressions

a $4t + 5g + 7t + 4g$ **b** $2x + y + x + 3y$ **c** $4m + 3k + m + 5k$

d $3x + y - 2x + 5y$ **e** $8m + p - 2m + p$ **f** $3n + 6t - n + 4t$

g $7k + 5g - 2k - 3g$ **h** $9d + 7b - 2d - b$ **i** $6q + 3p - 2q - p$

j $8g - 2k + 3g + 3k$ **k** $4x - y + 7x + 4y$ **l** $10d + 3e - 5d - e$

Answers
1 a $3p, p, 5p, 8p$ and $6g, 4g, g, 7g$ **b** $3q, q, 9q$ and $4m, m, 2m, 5m$ **c** $4x^2, x^2$ and $2y, 8y$ and $4t, 9t$
 2 a $11t + 9g$ **b** $3x + 4y$ **c** $5m + 8k$ **d** $x + 6y$ **e** $6m + 2p$ **f** $2n + 10t$ **g** $5k + 2g$ **h** $7d + 6b$
  i $4q + 2p$ **j** $11g + k$ **k** $11x + 3y$ **l** $5d + 2e$

Framework objectives – Using algebra with shapes

Use letter symbols to represent unknown numbers or variables. *(Year 7 objective.)*

Oral and mental starter

- Tell the class that they are going to work with ten. The complement of each number you give is what has to be added to that number to make ten. For example, the complement of 7 is 3.
- Start with easy integers first until they get the idea. 'What is the complement of 6?' (Answer 4).
- Then try 2.5 (complement 7.5). Ask in turn for the complements of decimal numbers, such as, 3.5, 8.5, 4.5, 7.2, 8.3, 5.4, 1.7, 9.4.
- After a few, stop and ask the students how they are trying to find the answers. Some will be adding on the decimal part to the next integer then building up to ten. Others will be using a subtraction method. Explore the diversity of methods, encouraging the students to use the technique which is clear to them. Ask them for a few more.
- Then go into fractions: for example, $3\frac{1}{2}$, $4\frac{3}{8}$. Again, stop after a few and ask the class for the way in which they are doing this. Is it the same method as they used for the decimals?
- Finish by asking again for complements to 10, but mixing up decimals with fractions. For example: 2.4, $3\frac{5}{8}$, 6.3, $5\frac{2}{3}$, 8.1, $7\frac{5}{6}$.

Main lesson activity

- Draw on the board the shape shown and ask the students for the perimeter of the shape.

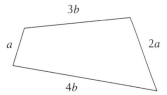

- Add up the lengths to get $a + 3b + 2a + 4b$, which simplifies to $3a + 7b$.

- **The class can now do Question 1, Exercise 5D from Pupil Book 1.**

- Put this next shape on the board.

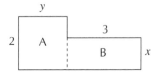

- Show how the shape can be split into two rectangles, A and B ($2 \times y$) and ($3 \times x$).
- Ask: 'What is the area of part A?' ($2y$).
- Then ask: 'What is the area of part B?' ($3x$).
- Show that the total area of the shape is given by:

    Area of A + Area of B

which gives:

    $2y + 3x$.

- **The class can now do the rest of Exercise 5D from Pupil Book 1.**

© HarperCollins*Publishers* Ltd 2003

Plenary

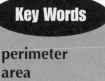

Key Words

- ☐ **perimeter**
- ☐ **area**
- ☐ **rectangle**

● On the board or OHT, draw the rectangle shown including its dimensions.

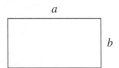

● Ask the class to write down its perimeter.
● Then ask them to write down its area.
● Next, put a compound shape on the board, or on an OHT (see below). Ask the class to explain how to find the shape's perimeter and area.

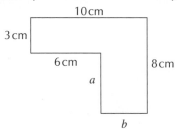

1 Write down, as simply as possible, the perimeter of each of the following shapes.

a 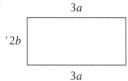 **b** 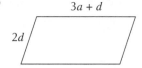 **c**

2 Write down the area of each rectangle.

a 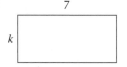 **b**   **c**

Answers
  1 a $6a + 4b$ **b** $6a + 6d$ **c** $3k + 5t$
  2 a $7k$ **b** $3h$ **c** tx

Homework

LESSON
5.5

Framework objectives – Expanding brackets
Multiply a single term over a bracket.

Oral and mental starter

- Ask the class if they can divide 420 by 15 in their heads without writing anything down, or using a calculator.
- It is most unlikely that anyone can. The answer is 28. If anyone is able to give the answer, get that student to tell the class how he/she did it.
- Explain that this can be done in your head in several ways. One way is to divide by 3, then divide by 5: $420 \div 3 = 140$, $140 \div 5 = 28$. Another is to divide by 5, then by 3: $420 \div 5 = 84$, $84 \div 3 = 28$.
  Another is to divide by 30, then to double the answer: $420 \div 30 = 14$, $14 \times 2 = 28$. Do explain how this works: to divide by any multiple of 5, you divide by 10 then double the answer.
- Get the class to try out the various techniques by putting a list of numbers on the board and asking them to divide each number by 15. Use the following list:
  345 (23)   465 (31)   240 (16)   390 (26)   645 (43)   525 (35)   195 (13)
  360 (24)   495 (33)   630 (42)   420 (28)   270 (18)   570 (38).
- After most of the class have used one of the techniques correctly and understand it, ask the class how they can tell if a number will divide by 15 before starting to divide. It must be both a multiple of 5 (end in 5 or 0) and a multiple of 3 (digits add up to a multiple of 3).

Main lesson activity

- Put on the board $5(3 + 4)$ and ask the class what value this has. When someone suggests 35, ask them how they calculated it (hopefully 5×7).
- Now show them that each term could have been multiplied out separately:
  $5 \times 3 + 5 \times 4$, which is $15 + 20 = 35$
  So, we can see that $5(3 + 4) = 5 \times 3 + 5 \times 4$.
- This process is called **expanding** or **multiplying out** a bracket. Go through a few more examples like this, such as:
  $2(4 + 5) = 2 \times 4 + 2 \times 5 = 18$ (check: $2 \times 9 = 18$).
- Show how to use this technique to simplify an expression, such as $4(m + 3)$:
  $4(m + 3) = 4 \times m + 4 \times 3 = 4m + 12$.

- **The class can now do Questions 1 and 2, Exercise 5E from Pupil Book 1.**

- Now put on the board $8k + 3(2k + 5)$ and ask the class how to simplify it. They need to expand the bracket and then to simplify the resulting expression by collecting and combining like terms:
  $8k + 3(2k + 5) = 8k + 6k + 15$
  $= 14k + 15$.
- Go through another example, this time involving negative terms:
  $4(3k + 2) - 5k = 12k + 8 - 5k$
  $= 7k + 8$.

- **The class can now do the rest of Exercise 5E from Pupil Book 1.**

Exercise 5E Answers

1 a $12 + 6 = 18, 3 \times 6 = 18$ **b** $15 + 5 = 20, 5 \times 4 = 20$ **c** $8 + 12 = 20, 4 \times 5 = 20$
   d $18 + 24 = 42, 6 \times 7 = 42$ **e** $40 - 16 = 24, 8 \times 3 = 24$
   f $50 - 20 = 30, 10 \times 3 = 30$
2 a $2x + 6$ **b** $8m + 4$ **c** $9k + 15$ **d** $10n + 4$ **e** $20 + 12t$ **f** $6 + 15g$
   g $6 + 18h$ **h** $15 + 10d$ **i** $9a - 3$ **j** $4 - 10c$ **k** $8 - 16f$ **l** $12 - 9b$
   m $6d + 4a$ **n** $20e + 10$ **p** $6x + 4y$ **q** $14q + 35p$ **r** $6q - 8p$ **s** $15t - 9s$
   t $28w - 12k$ **u** $20n - 15d$
3 a $16m + 8$ **b** $20t + 6$ **c** $13k + 28$ **d** $15g + 15$ **e** $11q + 12$ **f** $15h + 8$
   g $14f + 8$ **h** $11k + 10$ **i** $25t + 3$
4 a $6h + 15$ **b** $7t + 6p$ **c** $12k + 2m$ **d** $15g - 8$ **e** $7t + 12g$ **f** $17m - 8g$
   g $23m - 3k$ **h** $18p - 8m$ **i** $21h - 8p$
5 a $16x + 12y$ **b** $13p + 16m$ **c** $24k + 22g$ **d** $10d + 19e$ **e** $34n + 4p$
   f $29f + 6f$ **g** $13p + 8d$ **h** $13x + 2y$

Extension Answers

b Yes. Because the sum of three consecutive numbers starting from n is $3(n + 1)$,
   which is divisible by 3.
c Because the sum of four consecutive numbers starting from n is $2(2n + 3)$.
d Yes. Because the sum of five consecutive numbers starting from n is $5(n + 2)$,
   which is divisible by 5.

SATs Answers

1 a $780, 1300$ **b** 1040
2 a $7 + 5t$ **b** $3b + 17$ **c** $4d + 3a$ **d** $4m$
3 a $4n + 5$ **b** $3n + 4$ **c** 105

Plenary

- Ask the class what is meant by the word expression. Request some examples.
  Ensure that none include an equals sign.
- Then ask what is meant in algebra by the word expand. Ask for an example of a
  term outside a bracket and the process involved in multiplying the bracket out.
- Put two or three expressions on the board, all containing brackets. Ask the class
  to tell you how to simplify them.

Key Words

- term
- expression
- expand
- multiply out

Homework

1 Multiply out each of the following expressions.

   a $2(x + 4)$ **b** $3(4m + 2)$ **c** $5(2k + 1)$ **d** $3(5n + 2)$

   e $4(6 + 3t)$ **f** $5(3 + 6g)$ **g** $3(2 + 7h)$ **h** $4(3 + 2d)$

   i $5(3a - 2)$ **j** $4(3 - 5c)$ **k** $2(5 - 3f)$ **l** $6(3 - 4b)$

2 Expand and simplify each of these expressions.

   a $2(3x + y) + 3(5x + 2y)$ **b** $4(2p + 4m) + 2(3p + 4m)$ **c** $5(3k + 4g) + 2(k - 3g)$

   d $4(5e + 3d) + 3(2d - 4e)$ **e** $3(7n - p) + 2(3n + 5p)$ **f** $5(6t + 5f) + 4(2t - 3f)$

Answers
   1 a $2x + 8$ **b** $12m + 6$ **c** $10k + 5$ **d** $15n + 6$ **e** $24 + 12t$ **f** $15 + 30g$ **g** $6 + 21h$ **h** $12 + 8d$
   i $15a - 10$ **j** $12 - 20c$ **k** $10 - 6f$ **l** $18 - 24b$
   2 a $21x + 8y$ **b** $14p + 24m$ **c** $17k + 14g$ **d** $8e + 18d$ **e** $27n + 7p$ **f** $38t + 13f$

CHAPTER 6

Shape, Space and Measures 2

Framework Objectives – Perimeter and area of rectangles
Know and use the formula for the area of a rectangle; calculate the perimeter of rectangles. *(Year 7 objective.)*

Oral and mental starter

- This is a revision starter on perimeters and areas of rectangles.
- Divide the class into pairs, with each pair having an individual whiteboard or a sheet of A4 paper.
- Ask the class to draw a sketch of a rectangle that has a perimeter of 10 cm and an area of 6 cm² and hold up their solution once they have drawn it.
- The first pair to give the correct answer gains a point.
- Repeat the activity a number of times using different examples to suit the ability of the class.

Main lesson activity

- Draw on the board, or on an OHT, four different rectangles on a square grid.
- Ask the class which one has the greatest perimeter and which one the greatest area.
- Explain that when we know the measurements of a rectangle, we can find its perimeter and its area by using formulas.
- Derive the formula for the perimeter of a rectangle:
      $P = 2l + 2w$
- Derive the formula for the area of a rectangle:
      $A = l \times w$ or $A = lw$
- Stress the importance of using the correct units.
      The units for perimeter are: mm, cm and m.
      The units for area are: mm², cm² and m².
- Work through an example with $l = 6$ cm and $w = 4$ cm:
      $P = 2l + 2w = 2 \times 6 + 2 \times 4 = 12 + 8 = 20$ cm
      $A = lw = 6 \times 4 = 24$ cm²
- Work through another example with $l = 5$ cm and $w = 5$ cm.

- **The class can now do Exercise 6A from Pupil Book 1.** (Those students who reach the questions involving decimal lengths will probably require individual assistance with them.)

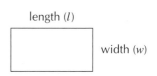

length (*l*)

width (*w*)

Plenary

- Write and draw on the board:
    P = 2*l* + 2*w*
    A = *lw*
- Ask students to find the perimeter and area of rectangles for different values of *l* and *w*.

Homework

1 Find the perimeter of each of the following rectangles:

a 8 cm, 5 cm **b** 15 cm, 4 cm **c** 12 mm, 18 mm **d** 25 m, 25 m

2 Find the area of each of the following rectangles:

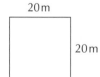

a 9 cm, 4 cm **b** 15 cm, 12 cm **c** 10 mm, 21 mm **d** 20 m, 20 m

3 The length of a football pitch is 110 m and its width is 80 m.

  a Find the perimeter of the pitch. **b** Find the area of the pitch.

Answers
1 **a** 26 cm **b** 38 cm **c** 60 mm **d** 100 m
2 **a** 36 cm² **b** 180 cm² **c** 210 mm² **d** 400 m²
3 **a** 380 m **b** 8800 m²

LESSON 6.2

Framework Objectives – The perimeter and area of compound shapes

Calculate the perimeter and area of shapes made from rectangles.

Oral and mental starter

- Draw the grid shown on the board or on an OHP.
- Ask the class to work out the largest number they can make by adding any two adjacent numbers on the grid. Explain that the two numbers can be from any row, column or diagonal.
- Now repeat this, but change the operation to multiplication.
- Repeat the activity, but now use three adjacent numbers from any row, column or diagonal.
- This activity can be extended by using larger numbers or grids of different size.

1	8	5
4	2	7
9	6	3

Main lesson activity

- Explain that a **compound shape** is a shape made from simple shapes, such as two rectangles (A and B).
- Show how to find the two unknown lengths a and b:

    $a = 8 - 3 = 5\,\text{cm}$ and $b = 10 - 6 = 4\,\text{cm}$

    $P = 10 + 8 + 4 + 5 + 6 + 3 = 36\,\text{cm}$

    Total area = Area of A + Area of B

    $= 6 \times 3 + 8 \times 4 = 18 + 32 = 50\,\text{cm}^2$

- Show that the area of the compound shape is the same if we choose two different constituent rectangles.

    Total area = Area of C + Area of D

    $= 10 \times 3 + 5 \times 4 = 30 + 20 = 50\,\text{cm}^2$

- **The class can now do Exercise 6B from Pupil Book 1.**

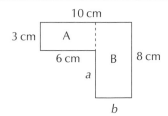

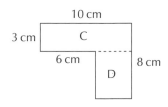

Plenary

- Ask the class to explain the meaning of *compound shape*.
- Ask a student to draw a compound shape on the board and write on some measurements of their choice.
- Ask other students to find the perimeter and area of the compound shape.

Homework

1 A room is to be fitted with a carpet. The room measures 12 m by 10 m.

   a Calculate the area of the room.

   b The carpet costs £8 for 1 m^2. How much will it cost to carpet the room?

2 Find **i** the perimeter and **ii** the area of each of these compound shapes.

a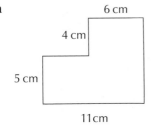

b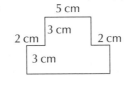

c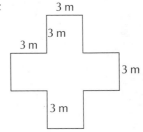

3 Four squares, each of side 4 cm, are to be cut from a piece of card measuring 15 cm by 10 cm.

   Calculate the area of the remaining card.

Answers
1 **a** 120 m^2 **b** £960
2 **a** 40 cm, 79 cm^2 **b** 30 cm, 42 cm^2 **c** 36 m, 45 m^2
3 86 cm^2

LESSON 6.3

Framework objectives – Reading scales

Read and interpret scales on a range of measuring instruments. *(Year 7 objective.)*

Use units of measurement to estimate, calculate and solve problems in everyday contexts involving length, area, volume, capacity, mass, time, angle and bearings; know rough metric equivalents of imperial measures in daily use (feet, miles, pounds, pints, gallons).

Oral and mental starter

- Ask the class to work in pairs or groups for this activity.
- Explain to the class that they have to make as many numbers from 1 to 10 as they can in about 10 minutes by using only four 4s and any of the mathematical operations +, −, ×, ÷, which may be repeated. Allow them to use the rules of BODMAS, but brackets may be used.
- Some examples are:

$$4 \div 4 \times 4 \div 4 = 1 \qquad 4 \div 4 + 4 \div 4 = 2 \qquad (4 + 4 + 4) \div 4 = 3.$$

Main lesson activity

- Explain that it is important to be able to read scales accurately on different measuring instruments such as rulers, weighing scales and thermometers.
- Draw on the board, or on a prepared OHT, the scales shown below. Explain to the class how to work out the size of each division or calibration. Then ask individual students to give the value at which each arrow is pointing.

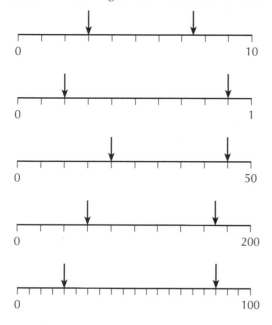

- **The class can now do Exercise 6C from Pupil Book 1.**

Plenary

- Draw on the board the scale shown below. Ask the class to work out the size of each division on the scale.

- The scale below can then be copied into the students' books.

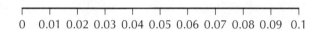

Homework

1 Write down the number that each arrow is pointing to on each of the number lines below.

a

b

c

d

2 Write down the mass that each arrow is pointing to on the scale below.

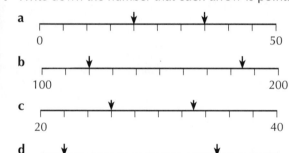

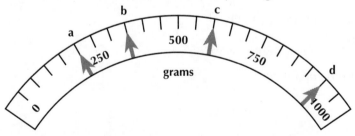

3 Write down the temperature shown on the thermometer below.

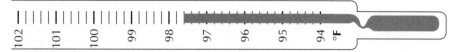

Answers
  1 a 20, 35   b 120, 185   c 26, 33   d 4.1, 4.75
  2 a 200 g   b 350 g   c 600 g   d 950 g
  3 97.6°F

Oral and mental starter

- Write the number 12 on the board.
- Ask individual students to come up and write on the board three numbers that have a product of 12, allowing repeats. Remind them that 'product' means 'multiply'.
- Examples are: $1 \times 1 \times 12$, $1 \times 2 \times 6$, $1 \times 3 \times 4$, $2 \times 2 \times 3$.
- Repeat the activity using different numbers.

Main lesson activity

- Work either with the whole class or with groups.
- Using an empty cereal packet, ask the class how to find the total surface area of the card used to make the packet (ignoring any tabs).
- Open out the packet to show the net.
- The packet is composed of six rectangles. Draw the net on the board to show this.

- Explain that the total surface area is calculated by finding the total of the areas of the six rectangles.
- Stress that this means *adding* the areas of the six rectangles, as some students will want to multiply.
- Notice that the six areas go in three pairs: 1 and 2, 3 and 4, 5 and 6.
- Ask the students to measure the length, width and height of the packet to the nearest centimetre to calculate the surface area. Remind them that the unit is one of area.
- Introduce the formula for finding the surface area of a cuboid:
  $$S = 2lw + 2lh + 2wh$$
- Ask the class to explain why the surface area of a cube is: $S = 6l^2$.

- **The class can now do Exercise 6D from Pupil Book 1.**

Exercise 3D Answers

1 **a** 280 cm² **b** 132 cm² **c** 310 cm² **d** 92 cm²
2 6 cm²
3 **a** 24 cm² **b** 150 cm² **c** 600 cm² **d** 384 m²
4 1238 cm²
5 62 m²
6 156 cm²
7 **a** 26 cm² **b** 22 cm² **c** 26 cm²

Extension Answers

3 Greatest surface area given by 20 unit cubes arranged in a straight line.

Plenary

● Draw a cuboid on the board. Ask the class to write down the formula to find its surface area.
● Do the same for a cube.
● Ask for the surface area for different values of l, w and h.

Homework

1 Find the surface area of a cuboid with $l = 20$ cm, $w = 8$ cm, $h = 3$ cm.

2 A cube has a surface area of 294 cm². Find the length of an edge of the cube.

3 The squares on the outside of a cube with edge length 5 cm are painted dark grey, light grey and white, as shown on the diagram on the right.

  a How many squares are coloured dark grey?

  b How many squares are coloured light grey?

  c How many squares are coloured white?

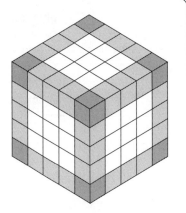

Answers
  1 488 cm²
  2 7 cm
  3 a 24 **b** 72 **c** 54

Framework Objectives – Converting one metric unit into another

Convert one metric unit to another (e.g. grams to kilograms). *(Year 7 objective.)*

Use units of measurement to estimate, calculate and solve problems in everyday contexts involving length, area, volume, capacity, mass, time, angle and bearings; know rough metric equivalents of imperial measures in daily use (feet, miles, pounds, pints, gallons).

Oral and mental starter

- A quick method to multiply a two digit number by 11.
- Write on the board:

    $24 \times 11 = 264$ $53 \times 11 = 583$ $44 \times 11 = 484$

- Ask the class if they can spot a pattern.
- Explain that the answer to the sum is obtained by adding the two digits of the number to be multiplied by 11 and placing the answer between the two digits.
- This method also works if the sum of the two digits is more than 10. In this case, the 1 in the tens column is carried into the hundreds column of the final answer, such as:

    $65 \times 11 = 715$ $46 \times 11 = 506$

- Ask individual students to make up their own examples and show these to the rest of the class.

Main lesson activity

- Remind the class of the common metric units and their conversions by writing on the board the following tables.
- Make sure that students know what all the unit abbreviations stand for.

Length		Capacity		Mass	
Larger unit	Smaller unit	Larger unit	Smaller unit	Larger unit	Smaller unit
1 km =	1000 m	1 l =	100 cl	1 kg =	1000 g
1 m =	100 cm	1 l	1000 ml		
1 cm =	10 mm				

- Discuss the processes of multiplying to **convert** from a larger unit to a smaller unit, and of dividing to convert from a smaller unit to a larger unit.
- Work through some examples of converting from one metric unit to another with the class:

    1 Convert 3.2 m into cm

    Larger unit to a smaller unit, so we need to multiply.

    100 cm = 1 m, so multiply by 100.

    3.2 m = 3.2 × 100 cm = 320 cm

    2 Convert 4500 g into kg

    Smaller unit to a larger unit, so we need to divide.

    1000 g = 1 kg, so divide by 1000.

    4500 ÷ 1000 = 4.5 kg

    3 Convert 2500 cl into l

    Smaller unit to a larger unit, so we need to divide.

    100 cl = 1 l, so divide by 100.

    2500 ÷ 100 = 25 l

- **The class can now do Exercise 6E from Pupil Book 1.**

Exercise 6E Answers

1 a 8 cm **b** 12 cm **c** 5.5 cm
  d 13.6 cm **e** 0.9 cm
2 a 200 cm **b** 1000 cm **c** 450 cm
  d 380 cm **e** 40 cm
3 a 3 km **b** 10 km **c** 3.5 km
  d 6.7 km **e** 0.8 km
4 a 400 cl **b** 700 cl **c** 150 cl
  d 820 cl **e** 30 cl

5 a 5000 g **b** 9000 g **c** 2500 g
  d 3200 g **e** 200 g
6 a 27 mm **b** 2200 m **c** 320 cl
  d 1100 g
7 4.1 m
8 4.79 kg
9 1200 cl
10 4.8 km

Extension Answers

1 1 km
2 1000 kg
3 11 days 13 hours 46 minutes and 40 seconds

SATs Answers

1 a 12 cm^2 **b** 3 cm^2 **c** 12 cm^2
2 a 48 cm **b** 3.8 kg **c** 103 cm
3 a A, C and D **b** 40 cm
4 100 cm^2, 80 cm^2, 32 cm^2, 252 cm^2, 252

Plenary

Key Words

- This is a quiz on metric units. Divide the class into teams and give each team a prepared sheet for their answers.
- Students within each team are allowed to confer and ask for a question to be repeated.
  1 How many millimetres in 5 centimetres?
  2 How many centimetres in 3 metres?
  3 How many centimetres in $6\frac{1}{2}$ metres?
  4 How many metres in 2 kilometres?
  5 How many metres in 1.6 kilometres?
  6 How many centilitres in 7 litres?
  7 How many centilitres in $2\frac{1}{2}$ litres?
  8 How many millilitres in 4 litres?
  9 How many grams in 8 kg?
  10 How many grams in 3.7 kg?
Answers
  1 50 **2** 300 **3** 650 **4** 2000 **5** 1600 **6** 700 **7** 250 **8** 4000 **9** 8000
  10 3700

- convert
- capacity:
  millilitre,
  centilitre,
  litre
- length:
  millimetre,
  centimetre,
  metre,
  kilometre
- mass:
  gram,
  kilogram

Homework

1 Change each of the following lengths to metres.

  a 200 cm **b** 800 cm **c** 550 cm
  d 320 cm

2 Change each of the following capacities to centilitres.

  a 3 l **b** 7 l **c** 4.5 l
  d 1.3 l

3 Change each of the following masses to grams.

  a 4 kg **b** 5 kg **c** 6.5 kg
  d 7.8 kg

4 The masses of three parcels are 2 kg, 750 g and 450 g. Find the total mass of the parcels. Give your answer in kilograms.

5 Richard cuts a 120 cm length of tape from a roll of tape that is 5 m long. How much tape is left? Give your answer in centimetres.

Answers
  1 a 2 m **b** 8 m **c** 5.5 m **d** 3.2 m
  2 a 300 cl **b** 700 cl **c** 450 cl **d** 130 cl
  3 a 4000 g **b** 5000 g **c** 6500 g **d** 7800 g
  4 3.2 kg
  5 380 cm

Algebra 3

Framework objectives – Linear functions
Express simple functions in words. *(Year 7 objective.)*

Oral and mental starter

- Put on the board the puzzle shown below.

      C A T S
      H A T E
      ———————
      D O G S

- Tell the students that each letter stands for a different number.
- Ask the students what they know about certain letters.
- For example, E = 0, both C and H are less than D, G must be even, and there are a few more sensible observations to be made.
- Ask for a suggestion for C, H and D. Then follow this suggestion through and see if it is a possible solution. There are several solutions.
- Once the class has suggested a correct solution, which may be after a few wrong attempts, ask them to work in groups of two, three or four to come up with a different possible solution.
- One solution is:

      4317
      5310
      ———
      9627

Main lesson activity

- Write on the board ADD 3 and tell the students this is a **function**. For different inputs ask what ADD 3 gives as the outputs.
- Write on the board some mappings, such as:

      2 → 5
      4 → 7

- Use about four inputs suggested by the class, or use 1, 2, 3 and 4.
- Ask the students to give you another simple function, but different. (You want one of subtract, multiply or divide).
- Repeat the same idea as above with a simple mapping diagram.
- Introduce the term **linear function**, and explain that this term is used for functions involving the four simple operations only (add, subtract, multiply and divide). All the functions that the students will meet in the next few weeks will be linear functions.
- Introduce the idea of a **mapping diagram** using two identical, horizontal number lines.
- Use the function ⟶ multiply by 2 ⟶, as in Pupil Book 1, page 78, with both number lines giving from 0 to 7.
- Show all the integer values and their images (outputs).
- Ask where certain fractions would map to, such as $\frac{1}{2}$, $1\frac{1}{2}$, $3\frac{1}{2}$. Then draw in their arrow lines.
- Explain that both number lines go on for ever, but only a small part of them is needed to illustrate the mapping.
- Also show the students that there are an unlimited number of fractions or decimal values that could be put on the mapping diagram, but it would look rather cluttered.

- **The class can now do Exercise 7A from Pupil Book 1.**

Plenary

- Put on the board a function such as ⟶ multiply by 2 ⟶.

- Show a set of consecutive inputs which contains large numbers such as 123, 124, 125, 126 and ask the students what they expect the difference to be between consecutive outputs – without working them out. Lead them to the difference being 2. You may need to talk the students through the correct outputs for them to see this pattern.

- Then write on the board a function such as ⟶ multiply by 7 ⟶, with

  another set of consecutive inputs which contains large numbers such as 135, 136, 137, 138, and ask what the difference will be between consecutive outputs. Lead them again to the difference being 7. Again, you may need to lead them through the outputs.

- If needs be, make the examples simpler so that the students can easily spot the patterns.

Key Words

- mapping
- function
- linear function
- coefficient

Homework

1 a Using number lines from 0 to 10, draw mapping diagrams to show each of these functions:

   i $x \to 3x$ ii $x \to 4x$ iii $x \to x + 3$ iv $x \to x - 1$

   b In each mapping diagram, draw the lines from 1.5 and 2.5.

Answers
   a i {0, 1, 2, 3} → {0, 3, 6, 9}   ii {0, 1, 2} → {0, 4, 8}
      iii {0, 1, 2, 3, 4, 5, 6, 7} → {3, 4, 5, 6, 7, 8, 9, 10}
      iv {1, 2, 3, 4, 5, 6, 7, 8, 9, 10} → {0, 1, 2, 3, 4, 5, 6, 7, 8, 9}
   b i {4.5, 7.5}   ii {6, 10}   iii {4.5, 5.5}   iv {0.5, 1.5}

Framework objectives – Finding a function from its inputs and outputs

Express simple functions in words. *(Year 7 objective.)*

Oral and mental starter

- Put on the board the puzzle shown below.

    B A K E D
    B E A N S
    ———————
    F I B R E

- Tell the students that each letter stands for a different number.
- Ask the students what they know about certain letters.
- For example, B is either half of F or half of (F – 1), and there are a few more sensible observations to be made.
- Ask for a suggestion for D, S, E, N, etc. Then follow through each suggestion to see if it gives a possible solution. There are several solutions.
- Once the class has suggested a correct solution, which may be after a few wrong attempts, ask them to work in groups of two, three or four to come up with a different possible solution.
- One solution is:

    45 907
    40 513
    ———————
    86 420

Main lesson activity

- Ask if any student can tell you what a function is. This should create some interesting answers. Try to draw out that it represents a rule for changing numbers and that each input to a function must an output.
- Write on the board 4 → 8 and ask what function maps 4 to 8.
- You should be given at least two answers ──▶ multiply by 2 ──▶ and
  ──▶ add 4 ──▶.
- Now put on the board 6 → 10. What is the function choice now?

  Clearly, it is ──▶ add 4 ──▶.

- Try another pair: 2 → 10 and 3 → 15. What function represents these mappings?
- Start with some trial mappings, such as 2 → 10 could be add 8. But add 8 does not work for 3 → 15.
- Next, try ──▶ multiply by 5 ──▶.
- This works for both mappings. So the function would appear to be
  ──▶ multiply by 5 ──▶.
- Now give the class {1, 2, 3, 4} → {0, 1, 2, 3}.
- They should spot ──▶ subtract 1 ──▶.
- You may need to go through one more example with the class, which could be, for example, {0, 4, 8, 12} → {0, 2, 4, 6} from the function
  ──▶ divide by 2 ──▶.
- **The class can now do Exercise 7B from Pupil Book 1.**

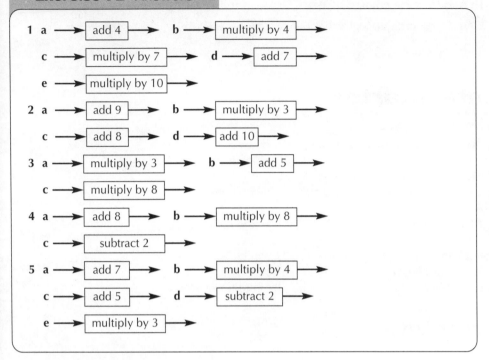

1 a ⟶ [add 4] ⟶ b ⟶ [multiply by 4] ⟶

  c ⟶ [multiply by 7] ⟶ d ⟶ [add 7] ⟶

  e ⟶ [multiply by 10] ⟶

2 a ⟶ [add 9] ⟶ b ⟶ [multiply by 3] ⟶

  c ⟶ [add 8] ⟶ d ⟶ [add 10] ⟶

3 a ⟶ [multiply by 3] ⟶ b ⟶ [add 5] ⟶

  c ⟶ [multiply by 8] ⟶

4 a ⟶ [add 8] ⟶ b ⟶ [multiply by 8] ⟶

  c ⟶ [subtract 2] ⟶

5 a ⟶ [add 7] ⟶ b ⟶ [multiply by 4] ⟶

  c ⟶ [add 5] ⟶ d ⟶ [subtract 2] ⟶

  e ⟶ [multiply by 3] ⟶

Extension Answers

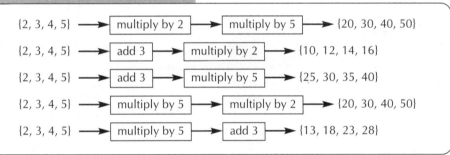

{2, 3, 4, 5} ⟶ [multiply by 2] ⟶ [multiply by 5] ⟶ {20, 30, 40, 50}

{2, 3, 4, 5} ⟶ [add 3] ⟶ [multiply by 2] ⟶ {10, 12, 14, 16}

{2, 3, 4, 5} ⟶ [add 3] ⟶ [multiply by 5] ⟶ {25, 30, 35, 40}

{2, 3, 4, 5} ⟶ [multiply by 5] ⟶ [multiply by 2] ⟶ {20, 30, 40, 50}

{2, 3, 4, 5} ⟶ [multiply by 5] ⟶ [add 3] ⟶ {13, 18, 23, 28}

Plenary

Key Word

☐ **function**

● Remind the class that finding a function concerns finding the rule that changes the given inputs into the given outputs. Emphasise the importance of their being able to identify a rule from the given values.
● Work through some more examples with the class, getting them to participate.
● For example, ask them to find each of the following functions:

    8 → 64, 9 → 72   Answer: → multiply by 8 →
    11 → 22, 12 → 23   Answer: → add 11 →

Homework

What are the functions that generate the following mixed outputs from the given mixed inputs? (**Hint**: First, put them into order.)

a {3, 0, 4, 1} → {3, 7, 6, 4}   **b** {4, 2, 5, 0} → {0, 4, 8, 10}

c {8, 9, 5, 7} → {4, 6, 5, 2}   **d** {4, 0, 2, 6} → {2, 0, 3, 1}

Answers

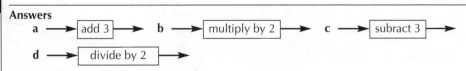

a ⟶ [add 3] ⟶ **b** ⟶ [multiply by 2] ⟶ **c** ⟶ [subtract 3] ⟶

d ⟶ [divide by 2] ⟶

Framework objectives – Graphs from functions

Generate coordinate pairs that satisfy a simple linear rule. *(Year 7 objective.)*

Oral and mental starter

- Ask: 'Who can divide 420 by 5 in their heads?'
- Tell the class you are going to show them how to mentally to divide by 5.
- First, divide 420 by 10, which gives 42. Then double this result, which gives 84. This should be verified with a calculator by one of the students.
- Ask the class if they can see how, dividing by 10, then doubling the outcome, works.
- Show them that dividing by 10 then doubling the result is equivalent to dividing by 5.
- Let the class try out the method on 320. Dividing by 10 gives 32, which is doubled to give 64. Again, have this checked by a student on a calculator.
- Try this out with a few more numbers, but make sure they are all multiples of 10.

Main lesson activity

- Talk about the way we have been writing functions such as

  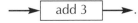

- Explain that a function can be written in different ways. For example, $y = x + 3$ is the same as ──►│ add 3 │──►.

- This is a simpler way of looking at the function when we want to draw its graph.
- The coordinates for drawing the graph of any function come from the combination of inputs and outputs. Tell the students that they are going to create some of these graphs.
- Write on the board──►│multiply by 3│──►. Then show the class how to work with $y = 3x$, where y is the ouput for different values of the input x.
- Next, show the class how to create a table that combines each input with the corresponding output. First, put on the board:

x	0	1	2	3		
y						

- Then show them how we to use the function to derive the values of y from those of x. Although any values of x can be used, it is easier to use small integers, such as 1, 2, 3, ….
- With the class, derive the values for y, writing them in the table:

x	0	1	2	3		
y	0	3	6	9		

- To draw the graph, a pair of axes is needed that use all the values in the table: that is, x from 0 to 3 and y from 0 to 9.
- Draw the axes on the board, showing the linear scale, and put all the numbers in.
- Remind the students how to plot the coordinates from the table, joining them up with a straight line.
- Point out that the straight line represents *all* the points that satisfy $y = 3x$. Demonstrate this by choosing any non-integer point, such as $x = 1.5$. Then go through the calculations $1.5 \times 3 \rightarrow 4.5$ and show that (1.5, 4.5) is on the line.
- Show that this works for a few other points also, say $x = 2.2$ and $x = 1.6$ (4.8).

- **The class can now do Exercise 7C from Pupil Book 1.**

© HarperCollins*Publishers* Ltd 2003

1 **a** 3, 4, 5, 6
2 **a** 0, 2, 4, 6
3 **a** −1, 0, 1, 2, 3
4 **a** 0, 0.5, 1, 1.5, 2
5 **a** 5, 6, 7, 8, 9; 3, 4, 5, 6, 7; 1, 2, 3, 4, 5; −1, 0, 1, 2, 3; −3, −2, −1, 0, 1
   d All the lines are parallel, and each line intercepts the *y*-axis at number following *x*
         in its function
6 **a** 0, 1, 2, 3, 4; 0, 2, 4, 6, 8; 0, 3, 6, 9, 12; 0, 4, 8, 12, 16; 0, 5, 10, 15, 20
   d Each line passes through the origin

Plenary

Key Words

- Write on the board $y = x + 1$ and $y = x + 7$.
- Ask what the students can tell you about the graphs of these two functions.
- They should be able to tell you that the lines have the same slope (are parallel), and that the first line intercepts the *y*-axis at a lower value than the second one.

☐ **coordinates**
☐ **axis**
☐ **parallel**

Homework

Draw the graphs of each of these functions.

a $y = x + 3$ **b** $y = 4x$ **c** $y = x + 5$ **d** $y = 3x$

Answers
   All four lines should be straight and should have gradients and *y*-axis intercepts of:
   a 1, 3 **b** 4, 0 **c** 1, 5 **d** 3, 0

Framework objectives – Rules with coordinates

Generate coordinate pairs that satisfy a simple linear rule. *(Year 7 objective.)*

Oral and mental starter

- Ask the class if anyone can give a shortcut to multiplying numbers up to 10 by 11.
- Hopefully, someone will suggest how easy it is and that a shortcut is not needed. For example: $6 \times 11 = 66$, $9 \times 11 = 99$.
- Next, ask if anyone can multiply 43 by 11. Show that first, 43 is multiplied by 10, giving 430, to which 43 is then added, giving 473.
- What about 56×11? This gives $(56 \times 10) + 56 = 616$. Have this answer checked on a student's calculator.
- Put a number grid on the board and point to some of the numbers to be multiplied by 11.

24	37	32
53	62	74
29	55	48

Main lesson activity

- Put on the board a grid with its *x*-axis from 0 to 10 and its *y*-axis from 0 to 6.
- Draw a tile, 2 units long and 1 unit deep. Tell the class to imagine they have 20 of these tiles, which are going to be put in a line on the grid.

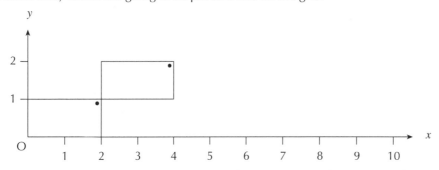

- Draw the first tile in position: one corner at the origin (0, 0); the corner with a dot at (2, 1). Ask the class for the coordinate at the corner with the dot.
- Hopefully the students will be able to say it is (2, 1). Remind the class of coordinates at this stage, if necessary.
- Put in another tile next to the first tile: one corner at (2, 1); the corner with the dot at (4, 2). Ask the class for the coordinates at the corner with the dot.
- Continue for two more tiles, placing the corners with a dot at (6, 3) and (8, 4).
- Put the coordinates of the corners with a dot in a list on the board.
- Ask the class if they notice anything special about the numbers in the coordinates. You are looking for these answers:
    'first number always even';
    'first number going up in twos, second number going up in order';
    'second number is half of the first number';
    'first number is double the second number'.
- Ask the class what the next four coordinates will be. Go through with them how they can now predict the next few coordinates without having to draw the tiles on the grid. They are (10, 5), (12, 6), (14, 7) and (16, 8).
- Ask the class: 'Will there be a dot at (30, 15)?'
  The answer is: 'Yes, because the second number is half of the first number.'
- Now ask the class: 'Will there be a dot at (28, 13)?'
  The answer is: 'No, because 13 is not half of 28).'
- Next ask: 'What will be the coordinates of the last tile I can put in place on this pattern?' You will need to remind them that you started with 20 tiles. The answer is (40, 20), show how the pattern develops: first tile – second number is 1, second tile – second number is 2, third tile – second number is 3, and so on, up to the 20th tile, for which the second number is 20.

- **The students can now do Exercise 7D from Pupil Book 1.**

1 a (6, 2), (9, 2), (12, 2), (15, 2), (18, 2), (21, 2)
 b First numbers are multiples of 3. Second numbers always = 2.
 c 41 is not a multiple of 3
 d (60, 2)
2 a (3, 2), (6, 4), (9, 6), (12, 8), (15, 10), (18, 12)
 b First numbers are multiples of 3. Second numbers are even.
 c 8 × (3, 2) = (24, 16)
 d (60, 40)
3 a (2, 4), (2, 6), (2, 8), (2, 10), (2, 12), (2, 14)
 b First numbers are always 2. Second numbers are the 2 times table.
 c 2 is the first number, and 22 is even.
 d (2, 40)
4 a (8, 6), (12, 9), (16, 12), (20, 15), (24, 18), (28, 21)
 b First numbers are in the 4 times table. Second numbers are multiples of 3
 c 10 is not a multiple of 3
 d (80, 60)
 e (8, 3), (12, 6), (16, 9), (20, 12), (24, 15), (28, 18)
 f First numbers are multiples of 4. Second numbers are multiples of 3
 g 16 is not a multiple of 3
 h (80, 57)

Plenary

- Put on the board the coordinates (1, 2), (2, 4), (3, 6), (4, 8).
- Ask a student for the next set of coordinates. It is (5, 10).
- Continue asking students for the next set of coordinates until you get to numbers which are too big for them.
- You can then ask a student for any starting set of coordinates.
- Ask another student for the second coordinate set.
- Then ask a third student for the next, looking for any pattern they may see.
- This too can be continued from student to student until the numbers get too difficult.

Key Words

- ☐ **coefficient**
- ☐ **gradient**

Homework

Vicky has 20 rectangular tiles like this:

5 cm
2 cm

She places all the tiles in a row. She starts her row like this:

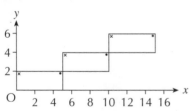

For each tile she writes down the coordinates of the corner which has a dot. The coordinates of the first corner are (5, 2).

a Write down the coordinates of the next six corners which have a dot.

b Look at the numbers in the coordinates. Describe two things you notice.

c Vicky thinks that (50, 20) are the coordinates of one of the corners which have a dot. Explain why she is right.

d What are the coordinates of the dotted corner in the 20th tile?

For each rectangular tile she now writes down the coordinates of the corner which has a X. The coordinates of the first corner are (0, 2).

e Write down the coordinates of the next six corners which have a X.

f Look at the numbers in the coordinates. Describe two things you notice.

g Vicky thinks that (30, 19) are the coordinates of one of the corners which have a X. Explain why she is wrong.

h What are the coordinates of corner with a X in the 20th tile?

Answers
 a (10, 4), (15, 6), (20, 8), (25, 10), (30, 12), (35, 14)
 b First numbers are multiples of 5. Second numbers are multiples of 2
 c 10 × (5, 2) = (50, 20)
 d (100, 40)
 e (0, 2), (5, 4), (10, 6), (15, 8), (20, 10), (25, 12)
 f First numbers are multiples of 5. Second numbers are multiples of 2
 g 19 is not an even number
 h (95, 40)

LESSON 7.5

Oral and mental starter

- Draw a circle on the board, and write the numbers 36, 25, 7, 3 and 4 inside its circumference.
- Also write on the board 518 in a box as a target.
- Ask the class to suggest a combination of some or all of the numbers in the circle, together with the four operations and brackets, that will give a total as close to the target number as possible.
- This works well with the students working in small teams of two, three or four.
- If you do have evenly balanced teams, you can play a few rounds and keep a score: on target scores 10, closest to target scores 5, next closest 4, and so on down to 0.
- In the different rounds, choose different targets and change the numbers in the circle.
- The beauty of this game is that the numbers do not have to be known beforehand, as the target number does not have to be achieved exactly.

Main lesson activity

- Ask the students where they see the most graphs (TV, papers, adverts, magazines).
- Many of these are travel graphs or distance–time graphs.
- Talk the class through Example 7.5 in Pupil Book 1 (but do not use the book for this).
- Write the key information on the board:
    Starting out from home: 8.00am, 0 km
    Arrival at post office: 8.30am, 4 km from home
    Time in post office: 15 minutes
    Leaving post office: 8.45am, 4 km to home
    Return home: 9.05am, 0 km
- Talk about the axes needed. The vertical axis is labelled 'Distance from home, (km)'. The horizontal axis is labelled Time'. Draw this pair of axes on the board and graduate the vertical axis from 0 to 4 and the horizontal axis from 8.00am to 9.20am.
- The plotting coordinates need to be identified to draw the graph:
    Starting from home (8.00, 0)
    Arrival at post office (8.30, 4)
    Leaving post office (8.45, 4)
    Return home (9.05, 0)
- Draw the graph of the journey, joining point to point with straight lines.
- You will need to explain that the slopes of the straight lines illustrate the average speed travelled at.

- **The class can now do Exercise 7E from Pupil Book 1.**

Exercise 7E Answers

1 **c i** 4 km **ii** about $2\frac{1}{2}$ km
2 **c i** 8.12am **ii** about 8.40am **iii** about 9.55am
3 **c i** 75 km **ii** about 320 km **iii** about 470 km
4 **c i** 17.5 km **ii** about 38 km

Extension Answers

Just before 10.04am
$1\frac{1}{2}$ minutes

SATs Answers

1 **a** (4, 2), (6, 2), (8, 2), (10, 2), (12, 2)
  b First numbers are the 2 times table; second numbers are always 2
  c 17 is not an even number **d** (3, 3), (6, 3)
2 **a** (8, 8) **b** (40, 40), (2, 2) × 20 **c** 25 is not an even number
  d (4, 3), (6, 5), (8, 7) **e** (14, 13) **f** 10

Plenary

Key Words

☐ **travel graph**
☐ **axes**

- Ask the students what their average speed is for those parts of their journey to school that they walk. This is usually between 5 and 8 km an hour, unless they dawdle.
- Ask whether they walk at the same speed all the time. Do they walk quicker uphill or downhill? Get them to discuss the notion of average speed, and why it is used on travel graphs.
- Ask a student to draw a travel graph of walking at 8 km/h. This would be a wiggly line that wanders about the straight line.
- Ask for other attempts at a true average 8 km/h.
- Discuss with the class why a single straight line is used to represent average speed.

Homework

Dean set off from home at at 6.00pm. He drove 80 km in 2 hours. He stopped for 40 minutes to pick up Helen, and then drove back home, ariving at 10pm.
a Draw a travel graph to illustrate this journey.
b How far from home was Dean at 7.30pm?

Answers
  b 60 km

Number 3

Framework objectives – Rounding

Round whole numbers to the nearest 10, 100 or 1000 and decimals to the nearest whole number of one decimal place.

Multiply and divide three-digit and two-digit whole numbers by 10, 100 or 1000.

Oral and mental starter

- Use a target board such as the one shown.
- Recall strategies for rounding to the nearest whole number and to one decimal place.
- Point at a number and ask students to round it to one or two decimal places, as appropriate.

4.56	2.37	1.07	3.22	0.54
0.08	1.62	14.65	3.99	4.81
3.42	8.52	3.68	9.02	1.03
6.45	1.45	1.29	5.92	2.71

Main lesson activity

- Ask the class for a number. Say they respond with 63.
- Produce a spider diagram on the board to show what happens when the number is multiplied and divided by 10, 100, 1000.
- The students should know the answers to this, but may need to be reminded of the rules about moving digits.
- Ask for the connection between the number of zeros and the number of places the digits are moved.
- Do a few problems, such as 7×10, $7 \div 10$, 0.4×100, $0.4 \div 100$, 0.06×100, $0.06 \div 100$.
- Recall the rules and explain how to do such calculations mentally.
- Repeat with other examples, introducing multiplying and dividing by 1000.

- **The class can now do Exercise 8A from Pupil Book 1.**

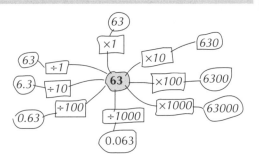

Exercise 8A Answers

1 a 4.7   **b i** 3.1   **c** 2.6   **d** 1.9   **e** 0.8   **f** 1.0   **g** 4   **h** 2.6   **i** 3.2   **j** 3.5
  k 1.5   **l** 1.9
2 a i 5   **ii** 4.7   **b i** 3   **ii** .3.1   **c i** 3   **ii** 2.6   **d i** 2   **ii** 1.9   **e i** 1   **ii** 0.8
  f i 1   **ii** 0.9   **g i** 4   **ii** 3.9   **h i** 3   **ii** 2.6   **i i** 3   **ii** 3.2   **j i** 3   **ii** 3.5
  k i 1   **ii** 1.5   **l i** 2   **ii** 1.9
3 a i 53   **ii** 530   **iii** 5300   **b i** 7.9   **ii** 79   **iii** 790   **c i** 240   **ii** 2400
  iii 24 000
  d i 50.63   **ii** 506.3   **iii** 5063   **e i** 0.03   **ii** 0.3   **iii** 3
4 a i 8.3   **ii** 0.83   **b i** 0.41   **ii** 0.041   **c i** 45.7   **ii** 4.57
  d i 0.604   **ii** 0.0604   **e i** 3478.1   **ii** 347.81
5 a 31   **b** 678   **c** 560   **d** 0.34   **e** 8.23   **f** 0.906   **g** 5789   **h** 0.5789   **i** 38
  j 0.0038   **k** 50   **l** 5.43

Extension Answers

1 a 4.72   **b** 3.10   **c** 2.63   **d** 1.93   **e** 0.78   **f** 0.99   **g** 4.00   **h** 2.60   **i** 3.19
  j 3.48

Plenary

- Write a variety of numbers on the board (for example, 32, 8, 0.09, 0.312, 48.9, 4598) and ask the class to multiply and/or divide them by 10, 100, 1000.
- Discuss the techniques used.

Key Words

☐ round
☐ decimal place
☐ tenth
☐ hundredth

Homework

1 Round these numbers to one decimal place.

  a 2.47   **b** 6.08   **c** 2.99

2 Write down the answer to each of these.

  a 4.8×10 **b** 0.56×100 **c** 7.92×1000 **d** $21 \div 1000$ **e** $214 \div 100$

  f $876 \div 10$ **g** 0.007×100 **h** $57 \div 100$

Answers
 1 a 2.5   **b** 6.1   **c** 3.0
 2 a 48   **b** 56   **c** 7920   **d** 0.021   **e** 2.14   **f** 87.6   **g** 0.7   **h** 0.57

LESSON 8.2

Oral and mental starter

- This starter is concerned with adding and subtracting 0.1 and 0.01 from other decimals and whole numbers.
- For this activity, it is helpful for the students to write on white boards.
- Give them an example, such as: 'What number is 0.01 more than 6.03?' (6.04).
- Now give more examples and ask the students to hold up the answer on their white boards.
- Suggested questions are:
    What is 0.01 more than 2.08? (2.09)
    What is 0.01 less than 5? (4.99)
    What is 0.02 less than 3? (2.98)
    What needs to be added to 3.34 to make 3.37? (0.03)
    What needs to be subtracted from 4.2 to make 3.9? (0.3)

Main lesson activity

- In the previous lesson, we dealt with powers of 10, such as 100 and 1000.
- Ask the students if they can name 10^2 and write it as a multiplication problem. They should come up with 'a hundred' and $10^2 = 10 \times 10$.
- Similarly, name and expand 10^3 (thousand), 10^4 (ten thousand), 10^5 (hundred thousand) and 10^6 (million).
- Ask the students if they can think of any other way we use these numbers. They should come up with column headings in place value.
- Put the following table on the board (which is reproduced in Pupil Book 1).

10^6	10^5	10^4	10^3	10^2	10	1
3	7	0	8	4	3	2

- Ask the students to read the number (three million, seven hundred and eight thousand, four hundred and thirty-two).
- Emphasise that large numbers are read as 'so many millions', 'so many thousands' and finally the last three digits. This is also why large numbers are written in blocks of three, previously with commas between each block. Commas are no longer used because of the practice in some European countries of using a comma as a decimal point.
- Repeat with other large numbers, such as 53 405, 203 405, 1 023 708, 12 007 009.
- Also ask the students to write out some large numbers which you read to them, such as:
    Sixty-two thousand, two hundred and six (62 206)
    Three hundred and five thousand and ninety-nine (305 099)
    Five million, seventy-eight thousand, three hundred and six (5 078 306)
    Two million, nine thousand and sixty-three (2 009 063)

- **The class can now do Exercise 8B from Pupil Book 1.**

1 a Four thousand, five hundred and sixty-one **b** Eight thousand and nine
   c Fifty-six thousand, four hundred and thirty
   d Twenty-two thousand, one hundred and eight **e** Sixty thousand and ninety-two
   f Three hundred and two thousand, nine hundred and ninety-nine
   g Three hundred and six thousand, seven hundred and eight
   h Two hundred and thirteen thousand and forty-five
   i Three million, four hundred and fifty two thousand, seven hundred and sixty-three
   j Two million, forty-seven thousand, eight hundred and nine
   k Twelve million, eight thousand, nine hundred and seven
   l Three million, six thousand and ninety-eight.
2 a 6 703 **b** 21 045 **c** 203 417 **d** 4 043 207 **e** 19 502 037 **f** 1 302 007
3 Spain 40 million, Germany 77 million, Italy 58 million, France 57 million, Ireland
   4 million, Denmark 6 million
4 a i 3 548 000 **ii** 3 550 000 **iii** 4 000 000
   b i 9 722 000 **ii** 9 720 000 **iii** 10 000 000
   c i 3 042 000 **ii** 3 040 000 **iii** 3 000 000
   d i 15 699 000 **ii** 15 700 000 **iii** 16 000 000
5 Both wrong. 'Just over' would mean less than $2\frac{1}{4}$ million. 'Nearly' would mean over
   $2\frac{3}{4}$ million.

Extension Answers

   a 240 **b** 360 **c** 7800 **d** 8200

Plenary

● Write on the board a variety of large numbers, such as:
    4 502 611   5 560 097   2 110 009   7 899 911
● Ask the students to read out the numbers and round them off to the nearest
  thousand, ten thousand, hundred thousand and million.

Key Words

  ☐ **place value**
  ☐ **column heading**
  ☐ **power**
  ☐ **million**
  ☐ **billion**

Homework

1 Write each of the following numbers in words.

   a 72 403   **b** 5 504 055   **c** 3 089 089

2 Write each of the following numbers in figures.

   a Seventy-two thousand, one hundred and sixty-one.

   b Two million, one hundred and three thousand, one hundred and six.

   c Eight million, six hundred and seventy thousand and eighty one.

3 Round the following numbers to **i** the nearest thousand,
   ii the nearest ten thousand and **iii** the nearest million.

   a 2 578 913   **b** 7 908 688

Answers
  1 a Seventy-two thousand, four hundred and three
    b Five million, five hundred and four thousand and fifty-five.
    c Three million, eighty-nine thousand and eighty-nine
  2 a 72 161 **b** 2 103 106 **c** 8 670 081
  3 a i 2 579 000 **ii** 2 580 000 **iii** 3 000 000
    b i 7 909 000 **ii** 7 910 000 **iii** 8 000 000

Framework objectives – Estimations

Make and justify estimates and approximations of calculations.

Check a result by considering whether it is of the right order of magnitude and by working the problem backwards.

Oral and mental starter

- The students can work in small groups. Give the students an OHP film and some OHP pens or a large piece of paper and some felt-tip pens.
- Give each group the same five two-digit numbers, say 21, 43, 54, 77 and 12 (use just four values if necessary, and the same five single-digit numbers, say 2, 3, 5, 6 and 9 (use just four values if necessary).
- In a timed session (say 5 minutes), the students have to write down as many multiplication problems as possible multiplying a two-digit number by a single-digit number. Calculators are not allowed.
- After the allocated time, stop students working and check the answers.
- Allocate a score to see which is the winning group.

×	21	43	54	77	12
2	42	86	108	154	24
3	63	129	162	231	36
5	105	215	270	385	60
6	126	258	324	462	72
9	189	387	486	693	108

Main lesson activity

- Using an OHP calculator or asking a student to work them out, obtain the answers to a variety of multiplication problems. For example:
  $$12 \times 46 = 552 \quad 13 \times 23 = 299 \quad 15 \times 24 = 360 \quad 19 \times 38 = 722$$
- Ask the class if they can spot a way of checking that the answers are right. For example, why must this be wrong: $26 \times 37 = 926$?
- Establish the rule that a correct answer must end in the same digit as that of the product of the original final digits: in this case, 6×7.
- Some students may also suggest that an answer can be estimated. For example, $12 \times 46 \approx 10 \times 50 = 500$.
  (Introduce the notation $\approx$ is approximately equal to.)
- Obtain approximate answers to, say, 13×23. For example:
  10×20, 10×23, 10×25. Which is better?
- Establish that there is no definite way to estimate. Numbers should be chosen that the students can deal with mentally. This will depend on their individual numerical skill.
- Now do the following as approximations. (Get student suggestions.)
  $304 - 138$ can be $300 - 140$, $300 - 150$, …
  7.5×2.5 can be 7×3, 7×2, 8×3, …
  Rules for dealing with 'halfway' values can be established. Should we go 'one up and one down'? For example:
  $40.8 - 29.7$ can be $40 - 30$, $41 - 30$, …
  8.76×4.79 can be 10×5, 9×5, …
- How can we check whether $510 \div 30 = 17$ is correct?
- Introduce the idea of inverse operations (for example: $510 = 30 \times 17$) which can be checked mentally.
- Similarly, $237 - 43 = 214$. Check if $237 = 214 + 43$. Answer: not correct.
- Addition is the inverse of subtraction and is usually easier to work out. Multiplication is the inverse of division and is almost always easier to work out.
- Using a scale marked with 10 divisions, estimate the value of a given point when the end values are known. For example:

- Key points: Establish the value of each division. Count on (or back) from one end.

- **The class can now do Exercise 8C from Pupil Book 1.**

1 **a** End digit should be 8   **b** Approx $50 \times 70 = 3500$ **c** Approx $100 \div 10 = 10$
   d $8 \times 35 = 280$ **e** $323 + 37 = 360$
2 **a** $2800 - 400 = 2400$ **b** $230 \times 20 = 4600$ **c** $800 \div 40 = 20$ **d** $60 \div 15 = 4$
   e $400 \times 400 = 160\,000$ **f** $160 \div 40 = 4$ **g** $70 \div 7 = 10$
   h top $40 \times 60 = 2400$, bottom $40 - 20 = 20$, $2400 \div 20 = 120$
3 Items are less than £3, £2 and £5, so less than £10 altogether. Change is 35p, 8p
   and 1p, which is 44p. Not enough
4 Each bottle is less that 50p, so 6 bottles must be less than £3
5 No: $8 \times 25p = £2$
6 53p entered as £53
7 **a** 2.7   **b** 4.2   **c** −10
8 Any reasonable estimate

Extension Answers

a The square is larger than a 6×6 square but smaller than an
8×8 square. The area of the square is equal to the central grid
squares (4^2) plus the four shaded triangles ($\frac{12}{2}$ each), giving
$4^2 + (4 \times \frac{12}{2}) = 16 + 24 = 40$ grid squares

b This square has an area of $6^2 + (4 \times \frac{7}{2}) = 36 + 14 = 50$ grid
squares

Plenary

● Write the following calculations on the board. Ask why they must be wrong?
  a $56 \times 36 = 2061$ **b** $38 \times 42 = 5196$ **c** $430 \div 6 = 55$
● Make sure the students know how to check the last digit, estimate and check
  using inverse operations.
● Write the following calculations on the board:
  a $\dfrac{39 + 47}{17}$ **b** $169.3 \div 26.4$ **c** 27.8×12.7 **d** $(58.4)^2 + (21.3)^2$
● Ask for an estimate of each. Discuss the 'best' way of approximating.
  For example:
  a could be $90 \div 15$, $100 \div 20$ or $90 \div 20$
  b could be $175 \div 25$ or $180 \div 30$
  c could be 30×10, 28×10 or 25×12
  d is clearly $60^2 + 20^2 = 4000$
● Make sure that the students know that there is not always a best approximation.
  The values should be chosen either for mental calculation or to avoid lengthy
  calculation.

Homework

1 Explain why these calculations must be wrong.
   a $63 \times 36 = 2286$ **b** $63 \times 36 = 3268$ **c** $714 - 68 = 654$

2 Estimate the answer to each of these calculations.
   a 21.6×38.4 **b** $184 \div 29$ **c** $\dfrac{52.3 + 39.6}{18.6 - 5.4}$ **d** $\dfrac{49.3 + 61.7}{26.5}$

3 Estimate the number the arrow is pointing to.
   a    **b**   **c**

Answers
   1 **a** last digit should be 8   **b** approx $60 \times 40 = 2400$ **c** $654 + 68 = 722$
   2 **a** $20 \times 40 = 800$ **b** $180 \div 30 = 6$ **c** $(50 + 40) \div (20 - 5) = 90 \div 15 = 6$
      d $(50 \times 60) \div 25 = 3000 \div 25 = 120$
   3 **a** 5.5   **b** −0.5   **c** 2.3

Framework objectives – Adding and subtracting decimals

Consolidate standard column procedures for addition and subtraction of integers and decimals with up to two places.

Oral and mental starter

- Draw on the board, or have prepared on an OHT, a grid such as that shown on the right.
- Tell the class that the aim of this game is to make 24 (or any target number given) by using adjacent numbers and any of the four operations. The numbers may be vertically, horizontally or diagonally adjacent.
- For example, 24 can be made in the following ways, using adjacent numbers from the board shown:

  8×3 6×4 $6 \times 5 - 6$ $3 \times (6 + 2)$
- Students can work on this individually or in pairs. The winning team is the one which comes up with the most correct answers in the time given.

8	3	1	5
6	6	5	2
7	4	6	1
9	3	2	1

Main lesson activity

- This is a consolidation lesson on adding and subtracting decimals without a calculator.
- A quick recall of methods should be sufficient. Emphasise the need to line up the decimal points and to use zeros to fill in any blank spaces.
- As an example, demonstrate the addition of 64.8 + 213.04 + 91.23 (= 369.07), showing the carry of digits.
- For another example, work out 23 – 6.78 – 8.7. This will need to be done in two parts: 23 – 6.78 = 16.22 and 16.22 – 8.7 = 7.52. Demonstrate the need to borrow and the use of zeros to fill in blank spaces.
- Tell the students that a package contains two items with masses of 1 kg 542 g and 2 kg 769 g, to which a third item is added to bring the total mass to 6 kg. Show them how to work out the mass of the third item.
- Demonstrate the need to put the numbers into the same units and to set up both an addition and a subtraction. That is, to solve 6 – 1.542 – 2.769, first do 6 – 1.542 = 4.458, and then 4.458 – 2.769 = 1.689. So the third item is 1 kg 689 g.
- As another example, find the perimeter of a rectangle with sides of 2.34 m and 76 cm. This could be done by doubling the sides or as an addition problem: 2.34 + 0.76 + 2.34 + 0.76 = 6.2 m.
- **The class can now do Exercise 8D from Pupil Book 1.**

Plenary

Key Words

- [ ] decimal
- [ ] hundredths
- [ ] tenths
- [ ] integer

● Write an example on the board, such as 23.4 + 5.406 − 3.4 − 1.08 + 2.367.
  Discuss the methods used and look at alternatives, such as adding all the
  positive values and adding the negative values before subtracting them. That is:
  23.4 + 5.406 + 2.367 = 31.173, 3.4 + 1.08 = 4.48, and then 31.173 − 4.48 =
  26.693.
● Refer to Question **1** part **j**, in which the positive numbers total 28.07 and the
  negative ones total 18.07. The numbers to the right of the decimal points cancel
  out.
● Discuss the advantages of working through such problems in stages or of
  combining positive numbers and negative numbers.

Homework

1 Work out the following:

   a 1.89 + 32.40 + 601.2   **b** 6.5 + 5 + 12.04 + 2.18

   c 16.23 + 12.39 − 11.18   **d** 51.3 + 18.2 − 28.61

2 In an experiment, a beaker of water has a mass of 1.256 kg. The beaker alone weighs 0.135 kg.
   What is the mass of water in the beaker?

3 A rectangle is 1.76 m by 39 cm. What is its perimeter?

Answers
  1 **a** 635.49 **b** 25.72 **c** 17.44 **d** 40.89
  2 1.121 kg
  3 4.3 m

Framework objectives – Efficient calculations

Carry out calculations with more than one step using brackets and the memory. Use the square root key.

Oral and mental starter

- As there is much to cover and a variety of makes of calculator are likely to be in use, this lesson does not have an oral and mental starter.

Main lesson activity

- Each student needs a calculator with square, square root and bracket keys.

- Without using a calculator, work out $\dfrac{37.8 + 7.2}{3.6 - 2.1}$ $(= 30)$

- Discuss how this is done. Emphasise the need to work out the top $(= 45)$ and the bottom $(= 1.5)$ separately.
- Make the point that the rule that separates the top from the bottom not only means divide top by bottom but also acts as brackets. That is, the above could be written as $(37.8 + 7.2) \div (3.6 - 2.1)$ $(= 30)$
- Now ask the students to do the calculation on their calculators. Ask for answers. These are unlikely to be the same. Answers of 30, 10.4, and 37.7 are possible (by 'sensible' erroneous calculations). Write these up and discuss how they are obtained. For example:

    $10.4 = (37.8 + 7.2) \div 3.6 - 2.1$ $37.7 = 37.8 + 7.2 \div 3.6 - 2.1$
- Demonstrate how to do calculations using the bracket keys. For example:

    $7.6 - (3.05 - 1.7)\ (= 6.25)$ $\dfrac{8.4 - 3.7}{8.4 + 3.7}$ $(= 0.388...\ )$

- Discuss how to calculate (on a calculator): 2.7^2, $\sqrt{625}$, and the remainder when 458 is divided by 24 (19 r2).

    Note Squaring can be done by the square key (usually $\boxed{\text{SHIFT}}\ \boxed{\sqrt{}}$)

    or $\boxed{\times}\ \boxed{=}$ or just by $2.7 \times 2.7 =$.

- **The class can now do Exercise 8E from Pupil Book 1.**

1 a 5 **b** 30 **c** 7
2 a $(17 + 8) \div (7 - 2)$ **b** $(53 - 8) \div (3.5 - 2)$ **c** $(19.2 - 1.7) \div (5.6 - 3.1)$
3 a 5 **b** 6.5 **c** 4.4 **d** 26.7 **e** 98.75 **f** 214 **g** 2.5 **h** 3.3
4 8, 8.7
5 a 6.5 **b** 8.3 **c** 6.76 **d** 15.21 **e** 9.5 **f** 1.4 **g** 11.56 **h** 73.96
6 a 6 **b** 14.55 **c** 16.4
7 a 42 r19 **b** 22 r10
8 $2\frac{1}{3}$ or $\frac{7}{3}$

Extension Answers

The $x!$ is called the factorial key and calculates, for example:

$3! = 3 \times 2 \times 1 = 6$
$7! = 7 \times 6 \times 5 \times 4 \times 3 \times 2 \times 1$
$\qquad = 5040$

The $\frac{1}{x}$ or x^{-1} key is called the reciprocal key and divides a number into 1. For example, 2 gives:

$\frac{1}{x} = 1 \div 2 = 0.5$

Plenary

Key Words

- Discuss the key presses needed to work out a problem such as $\dfrac{23 + 45}{12 - 7}$.

- Emphasise the use of brackets or the need to evaluate the numerator first.
- Ask the students whether they know how to use the memory keys.
- Demonstrate how to do this. (As there may be a variety of makes and types of calculator in the class, this may not prove worthwhile. Instead, ask them to investigate the memory keys before the next lesson.)
- Ask why it is necessary to use brackets in $30.9 - (7.9 - 6.4)$ and why not just do $30.9 - 7.9 - 6.4$. (This could lead to a discussion about $- - = +$.)

☐ calculator
☐ display
☐ enter
☐ clear
☐ brackets
☐ key
☐ square
☐ square root

Homework

1 First, estimate the answer to each of the following calculations. Then use your calculator to work out each answer. Round off your answer to one decimal place if appropriate.

a $\dfrac{368 + 103.5}{23 + 18}$ **b** $\dfrac{703 + 168}{54 - 21}$ **c** $\dfrac{803 - 397}{132 - 88}$

2 a Explain how you know that the answer to 23^2 is between 400 and 900.

b Without using a calculator, write down two multiples of 100 that 37^2 is between.

c Use your calculator to work out **i** 23^2 **ii** 37^2

3 Use your calculator to work out each of these.

a $\sqrt{5.29}$ **b** $2.3^2 - (7.9 - 3.2)$ **c** $(2.45 - 1.63)^2$

Answers
1 a est 11, calc 11.5 **b** est 30, calc 26.4 **c** est 10, calc 9.2
2 a $20^2 = 400$, $30^2 = 900$ **b** 900 and 1600 **c i** 529 **ii** 1369
3 a 2.3 **b** 0.59 **c** 0.6724

Oral and mental starter

● Have a set of 'Follow me' cards (30 are suggested below) that use multiplication or division by 10 or 100.

1	**START**. You are 3 ÷ 10	**2**	I am 0.3. You are 5 × 10
3	I am 50. You are 4 × 100	**4**	I am 400. You are 6 ÷ 100
5	I am 0.06. You are 11 ÷ 10	**6**	I am 1.1. You are 90 × 10
7	I am 900. You are 50 ÷ 100	**8**	I am 0.5. You are 6 × 10
9	I am 60. You are 9 ÷ 100	**10**	I am 0.09. You are 80 ÷ 10
11	I am 8. You are 9 × 10	**12**	I am 90. You are 23 ÷ 100
13	I am 0.23. You are 49 × 10	**14**	I am 490. You are 21 ÷ 100
15	I am 0.21. You are 76 × 10	**16**	I am 760. You are 52 ÷ 10
17	I am 5.2. You are 9 ÷ 10	**18**	I am 0.9. You are 20 ÷ 10
19	I am 2. You are 20 × 10	**20**	I am 200. You are 8 ÷ 10
21	I am 0.8. You are 18 × 10	**22**	I am 180. You are 2 ÷ 100
23	I am 0.02. You are 99 × 10	**24**	I am 990. You are 5 ÷ 100
25	I am 0.05. You are 66 ÷ 10	**26**	I am 6.6. You are 5.2 ÷ 10
27	I am 0.52. You are 7 ÷ 10	**30**	I am 0.7. **END**

Main lesson activity

● This work could be split over two lessons, one covering long multiplication, the other long division.

Example 1 Multiply 23 by 437. Students may have a variety of methods, all of which can be discussed. The likely methods are:

Box method (partitioning)

×	400	30	7	
20	8000	600	140	8740
3	1200	90	21	1311
				10051

Column method (expanded working)

```
     437
×     23
    8000   (400 × 20)
     600   (30 × 20)
     140   (7 × 20)
    1200   (400 × 3)
      90   (30 × 3)
      21   (7 × 3)
   10051
```

Column method (compacted working)

```
     437
×     23
    1311   (3 × 437)
    8740   (20 × 437)
   10051
```

Napier's bones or Chinese multiplication

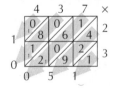

© HarperCollins*Publishers* Ltd 2003

Example 2   539 students and staff are travelling to a theme park using a fleet of 53-seat coaches. How many coaches will be needed? Discuss the operation (division).

Estimation gives $500 \div 50 = 10$

Solve using repeated subtraction ('chunking'). That is:

$10 \times 53 = 530$ giving $539 - 530 = 9$

So, 11 coaches are needed to carry all students and staff. The standard method of long division can be used if appropriate.

● Remind the students of the use of carry digits to help them do long multiplication. Emphasise that carry digits must be smaller than the other numbers to avoid confusion in the main calculation.

● More examples can be done on both long multiplication and long division if necessary.

● **The class can now do Exercise 8F from Pupil Book 1.**

Exercise 8F Answers

1 a 391   **b** 1344   **c** 855   **d** 2576   **e** 4152   **f** 17 312   **g** 3969   **h** 8307
2 a 36   **b** 42   **c** 27   **d** 25   **e** 24 rem 18   **f** 26 rem 18   **g** 28 rem 26
   h 19 rem 2
3 5916 people
4 39 trips
5 612 miles
6 3690 sheets
7 15 folders
8 a 16 runners   **b** £12 288
9 £15.75
10 £3480
11 250 shelves
12 8

SATs Answers

1 a 50→51, 60→57, 4000→3751, 1500→1537, 1600→1573
2 a Severn 400 km, Thames 300 km, Trent 300 km, Wye 200 km, Dee 100 km; Thames and Trent
   b Severn 350 km, Thames 350 km, Trent 300 km, Wye 220 km, Dee 110 km; Thames and Severn
   c 151 to 154 km   **d** 245 to 249 km and 251 to 254 km
3 a 12 168   **b** 13
4 a 1.2 m   **b** 1.15 m   **c** 170 cm

Plenary

● Recapitulate the methods with two examples that extend them.
   Work out 234×512 (= 119 808)
   Work out $3132 \div 54$ (= 58)
● Which method is best in each case? For the multiplication, use either the box method or the Chinese method. For the division, use the traditional (Italian) method.

Key Words

□ partitioning
□ long multiplication
□ long division
□ carry digit
□ column method
□ place value

Homework

1 Work out each of the following using any method you are happy with.

   a 45×54 **b** 176×26 **c** $912 \div 38$ **d** $900 \div 29$

2 a A baker bakes buns in trays that hold 32 buns. He has 27 such trays. How many buns can he bake at one time?

   b The baker has 924 rolls which he is packing in bags of 13. How many bags will he need? Will there be any rolls left over?

Answers
   1 a 2430   **b** 4576   **c** 24   **d** 31 rem 1
   2 a 864   **b** 71 with 1 left over

CHAPTER 9

Shape, Space and Measures 3

Framework objectives – Congruent shapes
Know that if two 2-D shapes are congruent, corresponding sides and angles are equal.

Oral and mental starter

● Imagine a square.
● Now imagine another square, exactly the same size, that touches the first one along all of one of its sides. What shape are you thinking of?
(Answer: a rectangle.)
● Imagine an equilateral triangle.
● Now imagine another equilateral triangle, exactly the same size, that touches the first one along all of one of its sides. What shape are you thinking of?
(Answer: a rhombus.)

Main lesson activity

● Remind the class about the different transformations they met in Year 7. The following diagrams can be drawn on the board or on an OHT:

A reflection in a mirror line   A rotation about a point   A translation

● Ask the class to describe what happens to the shapes after any of the three transformations. They should notice that the object and the image are the same shape and size.
● Write on the board:
'Two shapes are congruent if they are exactly the same shape and size. Reflections, rotations and translations all produce images that are congruent to the original object.'
● Have prepared sets of various congruent triangles and quadrilaterals made from card. With the class working in groups, let them sort the shapes into congruent pairs.
● Make sure the students understand that for each pair of congruent shapes the corresponding sides and angles are equal.

● **The class can now do Exercise 9A from Pupil Book 1.**
Card, scissors, tracing paper and square-dotted paper may be required for this exercise.

Exercise 9A Answers

1 **a** yes   **b** no   **c** yes   **d** yes   **e** no   **f** yes
2 **a** and **e**, **b** and **j**, **c** and **k**, **d** and **f**
3 **a** and **c**
4 **a** two different isosceles triangles, two different parallelograms, a rectangle and a kite.
    b a parallelogram and a rhombus   **c** a rhombus

Extension Answers

Examples of two congruent shapes:

Plenary

- Ask the class to explain what congruent shapes are. Invite students to draw two congruent shapes on the board or on individual white boards to show the rest of the class.
- Rotate one of the shapes and ask if they are still congruent. It may be best to prepare a grid if students draw on the board.
- Ask the class to describe what would happen if two shapes are the same, but are different in size. This should lead to a discussion on enlargements.

Key Words

- congruent
- congruence

Homework

1 For each pair of shapes below, state whether they are congruent or not:

a   b   c   d   e

2 Which of the isosceles triangles on the grid below are congruent?

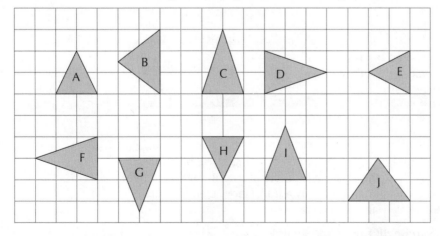

Answers
  1 a no b yes c no d no e yes
  2 A, E and H; B and J; C, D and F; G and I

LESSONS
9.2
9.3

Framework objectives – Combinations of transformations

Recognise and visualise the transformation and symmetry of a 2-D shape:
reflection in given mirror lines, and line symmetry;
rotation about a given point, and rotation symmetry;
translation;
explore these transformations and symmetries using ICT.

Transform 2-D shapes by simple combinations of rotations, reflections and translations.

Oral and mental starter

- Draw a large 'T' in the centre of the board.
- Ask a student to draw another 'T' anywhere on the board.
- Ask the class which 'T' is the object and which 'T' is the image. Ask them which transformation could have mapped the object to the image.
- Repeat the activity by allowing students to draw an image of 'T' in different orientations.

Main lesson activity

- This section includes a good deal of drawing for lower-ability students, so it is suggested that the work should cover two lessons.
- The first part of the lesson is to revise the three single transformations that the students have met, with an emphasis on congruency from the previous lesson. The examples can be drawn on the board or on a prepared OHT using a cut-out triangle.

- Reflections

  Triangle A is mapped onto triangle B by a reflection in the mirror line. Triangle A is congruent to triangle B.

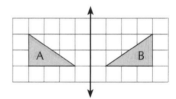

- Rotations

  Triangle A is mapped onto triangle B by a rotation of 90° clockwise about the centre of rotation O. Triangle A is congruent to triangle B.

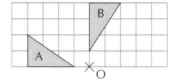

- Translations

  Triangle A is mapped onto triangle B by a translation of five units right, followed by two units up. Triangle A is congruent to triangle B.

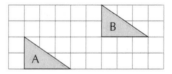

- Combined transformations

  Explain to the class that shapes can be transformed by using a combination of the above transformations. Show the class an example of a combination of two transformations, such as a reflection followed by a translation. Demonstrate this on the board, or with a cut-out triangle on a grid.

- **The class can now do Exercise 9B from Pupil Book 1.**

  Tracing paper and mirrors will be useful for this exercise.

1

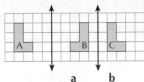

a   b

c translation of ten units right

2

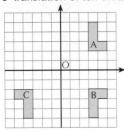

b   a

c rotation of 180° about the origin

3

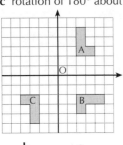

b   a

c rotation of 180° about the origin

4

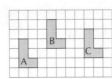

a   b

c translation of 7 units right and 1 unit up

5 a i a translation of 3 units right and 3 units up
    ii a reflection in the *y*-axis
   iii a rotation of 180° about the origin
   iv a rotation of 90° clockwise about the origin

  b i e.g., a rotation of 90° anticlockwise about the origin followed by a translation of 3 units left and 3 units up
    ii e.g., a rotation of 180° about the origin followed by a reflection in the *y*-axis
   iii e.g., a rotation of 90° anticlockwise about the origin followed by a translation of 5 units left and 6 units down
   iv e.g., a reflection in the *x*-axis followed by a reflection in the *y*-axis

Extension Answers

The following are possible examples for a combined transformation:

1 a a translation of 1 unit down followed by a reflection in the *x*-axis
  b a reflection in the *y*-axis followed by a translation of 6 units down
  c a rotation of 90° anticlockwise about the origin followed by a translation of 1 unit down
  d a reflection in the *x*-axis followed by a translation of 7 units left and 5 units down
  e a rotation of 90° clockwise about the origin followed by a translation of 1 unit left and 6 units up
  f a rotation of 90° anticlockwise about the origin followed by a translation of 6 units left and 6 units up

Plenary

- Draw a shape on a grid on the board, or use a cut-out shape on a grid. Ask individual students to use the shape to demonstrate the following transformations: a reflection, a rotation, a translation and a combined transformation.

Key Words

☐ **map**
☐ **transformation**
☐ **reflection**
☐ **rotation**
☐ **translation**

Homework

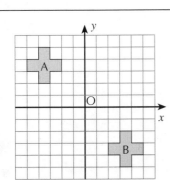

Find three different combinations of two transformations that will map shape A onto shape B.

Answers

Possible answers are:

1 A reflection in the *y*-axis followed by a reflection in the *x*-axis.
2 A rotation of 90° clockwise about the origin followed by a rotation of 90° clockwise about the origin.
3 A translation of 7 units right followed by a reflection in the *x*-axis.

LESSON 9.4

Framework Objectives – Reflections in two mirror lines

Recognise and visualise the transformation and symmetry of a 2-D shape: reflection in given mirror lines, and line symmetry.

Oral and mental starter

- Write on the board, or have on a prepared OHT, a grid similar to the one on the right.
- Ask individual students to complete any cell in the multiplication grid. Ask them if they have any particular strategies for working out their answer.
- Discuss some of the strategies used. For example, leave out the decimal point, then multiply and the answer will have one decimal place; to multiply by 4, double the number and then double again.

	×2	×3	×4
1.2			
2.5			
3.4			
5.6			
7.9			

Main lesson activity

- This lesson will give the class more practice on reflecting shapes.
- Explain to the class that shapes can be reflected in two perpendicular mirror lines – one after the other.
- Draw on the board, or on a prepared OHT, the following triangle on a grid with perpendicular mirror lines.

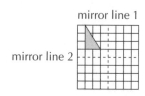

- Demonstrate reflecting the triangle in mirror line 1.

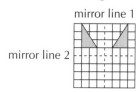

- Now reflect both triangles in mirror line 2.

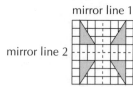

- The original triangle has now been reflected in both mirror lines.
- **The class can now start Exercise 9C from Pupil Book 1.**

Exercise 9C Answers

1 a   b   c   d

2 a   b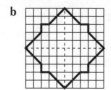

Extension Answers

Plenary

● Draw on the board, or OHT, two perpendicular mirror lines. Ask individual students to draw a sketch of a shape in any one of the four sections, and then to reflect it in both mirror lines.

Key Words

☐ **mirror line**
☐ **reflection**

Homework

Copy the following diagrams onto centimetre squared paper and reflect each one in both mirror lines.

1   2

Answers

1   2

LESSON 9.5

Oral and mental starter

● A revision exercise to remind students how to simplify ratios.
● Write the following ratios on the board, or on a prepared OHT, and ask the class to give the ratios in their simplest form (the students can either give oral answers or show them on individual white boards):

1 $3:6$ **2** $5:20$ **3** $8:12$ **4** $15:25$ **5** $24:36$

6 $18:24$ **7** $14:35$ **8** $30:50$ **9** $40:100$ **10** $45:60$

Answers   **1** $1:2$ **2** $1:4$ **3** $2:3$ **4** $3:5$ **5** $2:3$ **6** $3:4$ **7** $2:5$ **8** $3:5$ **9** $2:5$ **10** $3:4$

Main lesson activity

● The lesson is to show students how ratio can be used to solve problems that involve length and area.
● Remind them first how to write and simplify ratios

Example 1   Find the ratio of the line segment AB to the length of the line segment XY:

A ————————— B   X —————————————— Y
       80 cm   1.2 m

Since the lengths are in mixed units, change them to the smallest unit before simplifying the ratio. The ratio is $80\,cm : 1.2\,m = 80\,cm : 120\,cm = 2:3$.

Example 2   Find the ratio of the area of rectangle A to the area of rectangle B:

The ratio is $10\,cm^2 : 40\,cm^2 = 1:4$.

● **The class can now do Exercise 9D from Pupil Book 1.**

Exercise 9D Answers

1 a 2:5 b 1:10 c 4:5 d 1:5 e 1:4
2 a 1:3 b 1:3 c 1:9
3 a i 1:2:3 ii 1:2:3 iii 1:4:9 b they are larger versions of each other
4 a 1:1 b 1:5 c 2:5 d 1:2
5 a 1:8 b $\frac{1}{8}$
6 a 1200 m² b i 30 000 m² ii 3 hectares c 1:5 d 1:25 e $\frac{1}{25}$

Extension Answers

a 1:2 b 1:4

SATs Answers

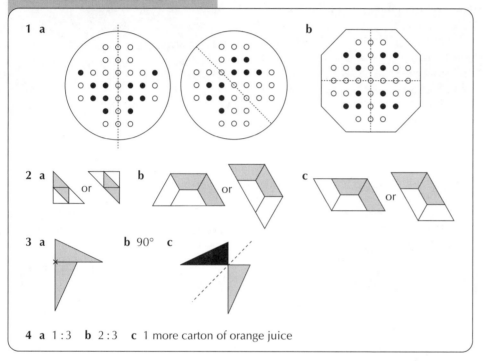

1 a   b

2 a   or   b   or   c   or

3 a   b 90° c

4 a 1:3 b 2:3 c 1 more carton of orange juice

Key Words

- area
- hectare
- length
- ratio
- simplest form

Plenary

- Ask the students to write a brief summary of what they have learnt during the lesson.
- Allow them to discuss their summaries in pairs or groups.
- Establish with them that the ratio of lengths and areas is different when comparing shapes.

Homework

1 Express each of the following ratios in their simplest form:

  a 12 cm : 16 cm   b 40 mm : 5 cm
  c 30 cm : 1 m   d 500 m : 2.5 km

2 Rectangle A is 6 cm by 2 cm and rectangle B is 6 cm by 8 cm. Find each of the ratios given below for the two rectangles, giving your answers in their simplest form:

  a the perimeter of rectangle A to the perimeter of rectangle B.

  b the area of rectangle A to the area of rectangle B.

3 A rectangle of length 12 cm and width 10 cm has a black square of edge length 2 cm in each corner (four black squares in total). If the four black squares are cut off the rectangle, find the ratio of the area of the black squares to the area of the remaining shape.

Answers
1 a 3:4 b 4:5 c 3:10 d 1:5
2 a 4:7 b 1:4
3 2:13

Algebra 4

Framework objectives – Puzzle mappings

Use letter symbols to represent unknown numbers or variables. *(Year 7 objective.)*

Oral and mental starter

- This is a puzzle for the students to work on in groups of two or three.
- Draw on the board the diagram shown on the right, or duplicate it and hand it out.
- Show that the sum of the top two numbers (3 and 4) is 7, and that the sum of the two numbers opposite is the same: 7.
- Tell the class that they must now complete the pattern so that the sum of any two adjacent numbers is equal to the sum of the two numbers opposite. They are not allowed to use numbers over 50 or to use any number more than once.
- The completed diagram is shown on the right. If some students are still struggling, help them by giving some of the missing numbers one at a time.

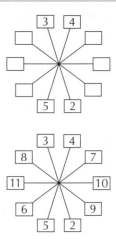

Main lesson activity

- Write $x \longrightarrow \boxed{\times 3} \longrightarrow 12$ on the board. Tell the class that this is a puzzle mapping.

- The puzzle is to find the unknown number x.
- Tell the class that an inverse mapping (opposite mapping) has to be found which will help them to work backwards to the unknown x.
- On the board, work through the solution with the class:

  $x \longrightarrow \boxed{\times 3} \longrightarrow 12$

  The inverse of $\times 3$ is $\div 3$. So, the inverse mapping is:

  $4 \longleftarrow \boxed{\div 3} \longleftarrow 12$

  which gives $x = 4$.
- Follow up with the solution to:

  $x \longrightarrow \boxed{+ 5} \longrightarrow 16$

  which gives:

  $11 \longleftarrow \boxed{- 5} \longleftarrow 16$

  That is, $x = 11$

- **The class can now do Exercise 10A from Pupil Book 1.**

1 a 14 **b** 5 **c** 10 **d** 8 **e** 14 **f** 15 **g** 13 **h** 9 **i** 3

2 a $x \longrightarrow \boxed{+4} \longrightarrow 9$

$5 \longleftarrow \boxed{-4} \longleftarrow 9$

$x = 5$

b $A \longrightarrow \boxed{\times 2} \longrightarrow 12$

$6 \longleftarrow \boxed{\div 2} \longleftarrow 12$

$A = 5$

c $y \longrightarrow \boxed{\times 3} \longrightarrow 15$

$5 \longleftarrow \boxed{\div 3} \longleftarrow 15$

$y = 5$

d $t \longrightarrow \boxed{+2} \longrightarrow 9$

$6 \longleftarrow \boxed{-2} \longleftarrow 9$

$t = 7$

e $m \longrightarrow \boxed{-3} \longrightarrow 2$

$5 \longleftarrow \boxed{+3} \longleftarrow 2$

$m = 5$

f $B \longrightarrow \boxed{-3} \longrightarrow 14$

$17 \longleftarrow \boxed{+3} \longleftarrow 14$

$B = 5$

3 a 8 **b** 3 **c** 7 **d** 6 **e** 4 **f** 2 **g** 11 **h** 6 **i** 3 **j** 3 **k** 6 **l** 8
4 a 7 **b** 5 **c** 9 **d** 17 **e** 5 **f** 3 **g** 30 **h** 14 **i** 4 **j** 21 **k** 7 **l** 25

1 Using only whole positive numbers and 0 gives 20 different ways
2 Using only whole positive numbers gives 16 different ways
3 An infinite numbers of different ways

Plenary

- Emphasise the importance of being able to use inverse mapping to find the unknown values in a variety of problems.
- Support the statement with a selection of examples which are worked through with the assistance of individual students.

Key Words

- [ ] **unknown**
- [ ] **solve**
- [ ] **mapping**
- [ ] **inverse**

Homework

Solve each of the following equations.

a $x + 7 = 13$ **b** $x - 8 = 10$ **c** $y + 5 = 19$ **d** $3s = 21$

e $4f = 12$ **f** $5q = 15$ **g** $p + 7 = 39$ **h** $5t = 40$

Answers

a 6 **b** 18 **c** 14 **d** 7 **e** 3 **f** 3 **g** 32 **h** 8

LESSON 10.2

Framework objectives – Puzzle mappings involving more than one operation

Use letter symbols to represent unknown numbers of variables. *(Year 7 objective.)*

Oral and mental starter

- Set the class this puzzle to be solved in groups of two or three.
- A farmer wants to get a chicken, a fox and a bag of grain across a river, but he can only fit one of them at a time in his boat. Also, if he leaves the fox and the chicken by themselves on the riverbank, the fox will eat the chicken. Similarly, the chicken will eat the grain if it is left alone with it.
- How can the farmer get all three of them across the river without loss?
- The solution is to take the chicken across, then the fox and bring back the chicken. Then take the grain across and finally the chicken.
- If some groups solve this fairly quickly, set them the following slightly harder puzzle.
- The farmer now wants to get two foxes and two rabbits across the river. He has a bigger boat, which can take any two animals at a time. However, if two rabbits are left unattended then they will fight, and if a fox is left with a rabbit, it will eat it. To make this explicit, the following combinations of foxes (f) and rabbits (r) may not be left unattended: rr; fr; ffr; frr.
- One possible solution is shown on the right.

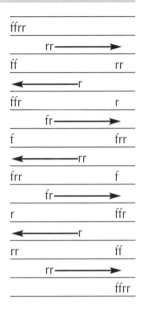

Main lesson activity

- Tell the class that today they are going to look at some mappings involving two operations.
- Put on the board:

$$x \longrightarrow \boxed{\times 5} \longrightarrow \boxed{+ 3} \longrightarrow 18$$

- Tell the class that the inverse operation needs to be found.
- Carefully show them the solution, getting individual students to give the inverse of each operation:

$$? \longleftarrow \boxed{\div 5} \longleftarrow \boxed{- 3} \longleftarrow 18$$

$$3 \longleftarrow \boxed{\div 5} \longleftarrow 15 \longleftarrow 18$$

which gives $x = 3$.
- Show that 3 will indeed map to 18 on the original mapping.
- Take another example to solve, such as:

$$x \longrightarrow \boxed{+ 2} \longrightarrow \boxed{\times 3} \longrightarrow 18$$

and create an inverse mapping:

$$4 \longleftarrow \boxed{- 2} \longleftarrow \boxed{\div 3} \longleftarrow 18$$

which gives $x = 4$.

- **The class can now do Exercise 10B from Pupil Book 1.**

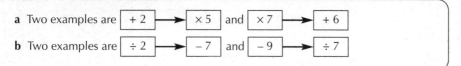

Exercise 10B Answers

1 a 5 b 2 c 4 d 6 e 1 f 1 g 6 h 5 i 7 j 4
2 a $x = 3$ b $y = 3$ c $t = 7$ d $w = 3$ e $m = 10$ g $g = 6$
3 a i 9 ii 1 iii 15 b i 12 ii 7 ii 13

Extension Answers

a Two examples are | + 2 | ⟶ | × 5 | and | × 7 | ⟶ | + 6 |

b Two examples are | ÷ 2 | ⟶ | − 7 | and | − 9 | ⟶ | ÷ 7 |

Plenary

Key Word

■ **operation**

● Put any double mapping on the board. For example:

⟶ | × 3 | ⟶ | + 1 | ⟶

● Ask a student to give a particular input, say 5. Then ask the others what will be the output (16).
● Now ask another student for an output, and ask the others to find the input.
● Repeat this several times.

Homework

Jenny has a number rule in her head.

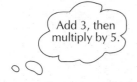

Add 3, then multiply by 5.

a What will be the answers that Jenny gives to these inputs? **i** 2 **ii** 7 **iii** 12 **iv** 17

b What inputs will give the following outputs? **i** 35 **ii** 55 **iii** 70 **iv** 90

Answers
  a i 25 **ii** 50 **iii** 75 **iv** 100 **b i** 4 **ii** 8 **iii** 11 **iv** 15

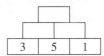

LESSON 10.3

Framework objectives – Solving equations

Solve linear equations with integer coefficients.

Oral and mental starter

- Put this diagram on the board:

| 3 | 5 | 1 |

- Explain that the numbers in two adjacent blocks are added together, and the total put in the box directly above. Do this with the class to end up with this diagram:

	14	
8	6
3	5	1

- Ask the class what numbers to start with in order to get 20 at the top. Let them try to work this out, either on their own or in pairs.
- There will be several different answers, one of which is:

	20	
5	15
1	4	11

- Now ask them what numbers to start with in order to get 25 at the top and have 8 somewhere in the bottom row.
- Again, there will be several different solutions, two of which are:

	25	
12	13
4	8	5

	25	
10	15
8	2	13

- You can continue with similar problems, such as getting 30 at the top with 10 in the bottom row.

Main lesson activity

- Put the mapping on the board:

$$x \longrightarrow \boxed{\times 3} \longrightarrow \boxed{+ 2} \longrightarrow 23$$

- Tell the class that this mapping can be expressed as an equation. Starting with x, *times by 3* gives $3x$, *add two* gives $3x + 2$. This is equal to 23. Hence, we can write: $3x + 2 = 23$. Explain that we call x the unknown.
- Go through another example:

$$x \longrightarrow \boxed{\times 5} \longrightarrow \boxed{+ 3} \longrightarrow 18$$

- Follow through this mapping to get to the equation $5x + 3 = 18$.
- Now reverse the procedure. Put on the board the equation $4x + 5 = 17$, and ask for the mapping. It should be:

$$x \longrightarrow \boxed{\times 4} \longrightarrow \boxed{+ 5} \longrightarrow 17$$

- Go through another equation: $6x - 1 = 23$. This will give the mapping:

$$x \longrightarrow \boxed{\times 6} \longrightarrow \boxed{- 1} \longrightarrow 23$$

- Now explain to the class that these equations can be solved by looking at their mapping diagrams.

- For example, put on the board $5x - 4 = 11$. Get the students to give its mapping diagram

$$x \longrightarrow \boxed{\times 5} \longrightarrow \boxed{-4} \longrightarrow 11$$

- Explain that the inverse mapping is now put down to solve the equation, as in the last lesson. This inverse mapping will be:

$$3 \longleftarrow \boxed{\div 3} \longleftarrow \boxed{+4} \longleftarrow 11$$

- This gives the solution $x = 3$.
- Go through a similar process with $4x + 2 = 22$, to obtain the solution $x = 5$.

- **The class can now do Exercise 10C from Pupil Book 1.**

Exercise 10C Answers

1 a i $2x + 3 = 11$ **ii** 4 **b i** $3x + 1 = 16$ **ii** 5 **c i** $5t + 4 = 34$ **ii** 6
 d i $4t - 3 = 13$ **ii** 4 **e i** $2y - 1 = 13$ **ii** 7 **f i** $7y + 5 = 26$ **ii** 3

2 a $x \longrightarrow \boxed{\times 3} \longrightarrow \boxed{+4} \longrightarrow 19$ **b** $x \longrightarrow \boxed{\times 2} \longrightarrow \boxed{+5} \longrightarrow 11$

   $5 \longleftarrow \boxed{\div 3} \longleftarrow \boxed{-4} \longleftarrow 19$ $3 \longleftarrow \boxed{\div 2} \longleftarrow \boxed{-5} \longleftarrow 11$

   $x = 5$ $x = 3$

c $x \longrightarrow \boxed{\times 4} \longrightarrow \boxed{-1} \longrightarrow 23$ **d** $x \longrightarrow \boxed{\times 5} \longrightarrow \boxed{-3} \longrightarrow 17$

   $6 \longleftarrow \boxed{\div 4} \longleftarrow \boxed{+1} \longleftarrow 23$ $4 \longleftarrow \boxed{\div 5} \longleftarrow \boxed{+3} \longleftarrow 17$

   $x = 6$ $x = 4$

e $x \longrightarrow \boxed{\times 3} \longrightarrow \boxed{+1} \longrightarrow 22$ **f** $x \longrightarrow \boxed{\times 6} \longrightarrow \boxed{-5} \longrightarrow 7$

   $7 \longleftarrow \boxed{\div 3} \longleftarrow \boxed{-1} \longleftarrow 22$ $2 \longleftarrow \boxed{\div 6} \longleftarrow \boxed{+5} \longleftarrow 7$

   $x = 7$ $x = 2$

3 a 6 **b** 7 **c** 7 **d** 7 **e** 8 **f** 10
4 a 7 **b** 5 **c** 3 **d** 8 **e** 3 **f** 3 **g** 2 **h** 6 **i** 4 **j** 11 **k** 9 **l** 7

Extension Answers

a i 33 **ii** 27 **iii** 21 **b i** 6 **ii** 8 **iii** 9 **c** −0.6

Plenary

Key Word

- Remind the class that all the equations they have met so far have had whole-number answers.
- Tell them that this is not always the case: for example, $10x + 3 = 11$.
- Go through the mapping and the inverse mapping to solve this equation.
- It will involve division of 8 by 10, which hopefully the class will be able to work out as 0.8. Some may need a calculator to show this.

☐ **unknown**

Homework

i Write down the mapping that gives each of the following equations.

ii Use inverse mapping to solve each equation.

a $4x + 5 = 17$ **b** $3x - 4 = 17$ **c** $2x - 3 = 17$ **d** $5x + 2 = 17$

e $10x + 3 = 20$ **f** $10x - 2 = 21$

Answers

a 3 **b** 7 **c** 10 **d** 3 **e** 1.7 **f** 2.3

Oral and mental starter

- Ask one of the students for an even number between 100 and 200. For example, 132.
- Ask them to halve this number (66).
- Discuss with the class the different ways they halved. This may be 50 + 15 + 1 or 60 + 5 + 1, as well as other ways which may be suggested.
- If the half is an even number, ask them to halve it again. Continue halving until an odd number is reached.
- Now ask the class for an even number between 100 and 200 that they can halve several times.
- Try out each of their suggestions, keeping a record on the board of how many times each number is halved.128 is the number which gives the largest number of halves (seven times before 1 is reached).192 is the next-best with six times.

Main lesson activity

- Write on the board an expression such as $7x$. Ask the class what it is.
- Many will say $7x$, or seven times x, but you want to draw out the answer **expression** . (If they cannot guess the name, you could try playing a part game of hangman in order to get to the word).
- Explain that the letter x can take any value we wish, and is therefore called a **variable**. For each different value of x, there will be a different value of the expression.
- Make a simple table of $x \rightarrow 7x$. Write in the different values suggested by the class beneath the heading x and the resulting values of $7x$. Include some negative values.
- Explain that in each case a number has been **substituted** for the variable x.
- Ask the class to suggest another expression and repeat the table.
- Ask if these tables look familiar, and link back to functions and mappings.
- Repeat with $\frac{x}{2}$ and $3a + 5b$, including small negative numbers.
- **The class can now do Exercise 10D from Pupil Book 1.**

Plenary

Key Words

- Put up a list of expressions for the class to evaluate.
- Then ask the class to provide expressions that give, for example, the value 5. Repeat with a range of values.

☐ **expression**
☐ **substitution**
☐ **variable**

Homework

1 If $a = 3$ and $b = 5$, find the value of each of the following.

   a $2a + b$ b $3a − b$ c $2b + 3a$ d $2b − a$

2 If $c = 7$ and $d = −1$, find the value of each of the following.

   a $5c + d$ b $8c − 3d$ c $4d + 5c$ d $2d − c$

Answers

1 a 11   b 4   c 19   d 7
2 a 34   b 53   c 31   d −9

Oral and mental starter

- This is a puzzle that is best thought about individually.
- I was in a shop the other day when the man in front of me asked for:
  'Some 20p balloons, six times as many 10p balloons and make up the rest in 25p balloons.'
  He handed over £6 with the statement: 'No change, please.'
- How did the shopkeeper sort out the number of balloons?
- Ask the class to find the solution, reminding them that there must be no change and no overcharging.
- The solution is five 20p balloons, thirty 10p balloons and eight 25p balloons.
- A strategy to find the solution using algebra is to let the number of 20p balloons be x. Then there will be $6x$ balloons at 10p and the rest at 25p. Therefore, the cost of the 20p balloons is $20x$, and the cost of the 10p balloons is $60x$. The total cost of both is $80x$.
- The remainder of the £6 must go on 25p balloons. So, to get no change, $80x$ must be a multiple of 25p. By trying $x = 1$, $x = 2$, $x = 3$, …, it is found that $x = 5$ gives $80x = 400$, which is a multiple of 25p. Therefore, the solution is five 20p balloons, thirty 10p balloons and eight 25p balloons.

Main lesson activity

- Ask if anyone can remember what a **formula** is.
- Draw from the class that a formula is an equation which states the connection between one or more quantities, each of which is represented by a different letter called a variable.
- Show the formula for converting a mass in kilograms into a mass in pounds:

  $P = 2.2K$

- Use the formula to convert 10 kilograms. That is, $K = 10$, which gives

  $P = 2.2 \times 10 = 22$ pounds

- Ask the class if anyone can think of a formula which uses more than one variable to work out another. For example, the formula for the volume of a box ($V = bwh$).
- Use this to illustrate how to substitute into the formula to calculate one value from two others. In $V = bwh$, b is the lenght of the box, w is the width and h is its height. So, calculate the volume for $b = 5$ cm, $w = 2$ cm and $h = 8$ cm, which gives:

  $V = 5 \times 2 \times 8 = 80 \, \text{cm}^3$

- **The class can now do Exercise 10E from Pupil Book 1.**

Plenary

- Ask the class if they know any formulae to do with perimeter, area and surface area. Write them on the board. They should be able to recall those for rectangles and cuboids from Chapter 6 – Shape, Space and Measures 2. Make sure they know what each letter stands for.

Key Words

- formula
- variable

Homework

1 If $M = DV$, find M when **i** $D = 2$ and $V = 150$ **ii** $D = 7$ and $V = 200$

2 If $A = 4rh$, find A when **i** $r = 15$ and $h = 5$ **ii** $r = 20$ and $h = 16$

3 If $n = \dfrac{A + 360}{180}$, find n when **i** $A = 180$ **ii** $A = 720$

4 If $U = v - ft$, find U when **i** $v = 80, f = 32$ and $t = 2$ **ii** $v = 120, f = 15$ and $t = 6$

5 If $L = \dfrac{A}{B}$, find L when **i** $A = 36$ and $B = 4$ **ii** $A = 10$ and $B = 2$

6 $T = \dfrac{P(q - r)}{2}$, find T when $P = 14$, $q = 19$ and $r = 11$

Answers
1 **i** 300 **ii** 1400
2 **i** 300 **ii** 1280
3 **i** 3 **ii** 6
4 **i** 16 **ii** 30
5 **i** 9 **ii** 5
6 56

LESSON 10.6

Framework objectives – Creating your own expressions and formulae

Derive simple formulae.

Oral and mental starter

- This puzzle is best tackled in groups of two or three.
- Draw on the board the 3 by 3 square shown.
- Show that the three-digit number in the second row is twice that in the top row; the number in the bottom row is three times that in the top row; and that all the digits from 1 to 9 have been used.
- There are three other ways of arranging the digits 1 to 9 like this. Ask the class to find them.
- Their strategy should include recognising that the first digit in the top left-hand corner must be one of 1, 2 or 3.
- Other hints can include: 'Start with the top right-hand digit, which gives you three of the digits.'
- The three other possible starting numbers are 219, 273 and 327.

1	9	2
3	8	4
5	7	6

Main lesson activity

- Start the lesson by asking the question: 'Can you give me four consecutive whole numbers that add up to 100?'
- After a few guesses have been given, explain to the class that today they are going to try to create an equation which describes a situation.
- Return to the four consecutive number problem. Start with the first number, and call it n.
- 'What will the number be that is one more than n?' The class should realise it is $(n + 1)$.
- 'What is the number one more than that?' The class should give $(n + 1 + 1) = (n + 2)$.
- Similarly, the fourth number is $(n + 3)$.
- Now add these together, to give $n + (n + 1) + (n + 2) + (n + 3)$.
- So four consecutive numbers added together can be written as:
    $S = 4n + 6$.
- To find which four consecutive numbers sum to 100, write the equation $4n + 6 = 100$, which leads to $4n = 94$. This has the solution $n = 23.5$. In other words, no four consecutive numbers have the total 100.
- Go through another situation. Ask how many months there are in a year (12).
- Ask how many months there are in 5 years ($5 \times 12 = 60$ months).
- Finally ask how many months there are in t years.
- You will need to discuss this question and its answer of $12t$.

- **The class can now do Exercise 10F from Pupil Book 1.**

Exercise 10F Answers

1 a $S = a + b + c$ b $P = xy$ c $D = a - b$ d $S = 4n + 6$ e $D = 7W$ f $A = \dfrac{(m + n + p)}{3}$
2 a 7 b 21 c $7w$
3 a i 14 ii 18 iii $13 + t$ b i 12 ii 10 iii $13 - m$
4 a 30 b 60 c $30t$
5 a 1000 b 5000 c $1000x$
6 $60m$
7 i 10 ii 3 iii $\frac{b}{2}$
8 i 8 ii 14 iii $2T$
9 bk
10 a 210 pence b $35k$ pence c kq pence
11 a $6b$ b $7b + 2y$
12 $16 + 3x$

Plenary

Key Words

● Ask the class what the first five odd numbers add up to (25).
● Ask them what the first ten odd numbers add up to (100).
● Tell the class that you are super-quick on a calculator and can add up any number of odd numbers on a calculator in, say, 5 seconds.
● Ask the class to set you a target, n, less than 50, and you will add up the first n odd numbers. (The answer is simply n^2.) Write your answer on a piece of paper and give this to a student while the rest of the class calculate the total.
● Once a number of students have worked out the total for themselves, reveal that your answer is the same. Let them know the formula that you used.

consecutive
expression

Homework

1 Using the letters suggested, construct a simple formula in each case.

  a The sum, S, of four numbers a, b, c and d. **b** The product, P, of two numbers A and B.

  c The sum, S, of five consecutive integers.

2 Give the number of hours in: **a** 4 days **b** d days

3 A boy is now 15 years old.

  a How many years old he will be in: **i** 6 years **ii** t years?

  b How many years old was he: **i** 7 years ago **ii** n years ago?

4 Give how many metres there are in: **a** 7 km **b** y km

5 How many seconds are there in t minutes?

6 Write down the number that is three times as big as K.

Answers
  1 a $S = a + b + c + d$ **b** $P = AB$ **c** $S = 5n + 10$
  2 a 96 **b** 24d
  3 a i 21 **ii** 15 + t **b i** 8 **ii** 15 − n
  4 a 7000 **b** 1000y
  5 60t
  6 3K

Handling Data 2

Framework objectives – Statistical surveys

Discuss a problem that can be addressed by statistical methods and identify related questions to explore.

Decide which data to collect to answer a question, and the degree of accuracy needed. Identify possible sources.

Plan how to collect the data, including sample size. Design and use two-way tables for discrete data.

Collect data using a suitable method, such as observation, controlled experiment using ICT, or questionnaire.

Communicate orally and on paper the results of a statistical enquiry and the methods used, using ICT as appropriate. Justify the choice of what is presented.

Oral and mental starter

- Write on the board or on an OHT: 'Children eat more junk food than adults.'
- Ask the class how they would investigate this statement to try to establish whether there is any truth in it.
- Encourage them to come up with answers to do with surveys, questionnaires or even an experiment in which they ask people to record what they eat over, say, one week.
- Write down any key words on the board for them to use later.
- Discuss how, as a class, they could use different approaches to the investigation.

Main lesson activity

- This work could be time consuming and it is suggested that it should take at least two lessons to complete. (See also Lesson 11.5.)
- The results could be used for display work or possibly for small groups to do short presentations.
- Show them a problem statement, for example:
    'Children eat more junk food than adults'
- Tell them that you are going to carry out a quick survey amongst the class to try to find out if they think that the statement is true.
- Ask them to put up their hands if they eat burgers at least once a week. Record the response on the board.
- Now ask them how many have school lunch, and record how many of those are likely to have or to have had chips with their lunch.
- Point out that so far you have been finding out information or data about young people.
- Now ask them the question: 'Do you think that children eat more junk food than adults?'
- Record the results.
- Point out that some people may not want to answer certain questions because they find them embarrassing or too personal.
- Explain that it is important to keep questions short and simple, and to avoid asking personal questions.
- Explain to the class that they will be looking at statements in Pupil Book 1 and making up questions that they could ask. This work could be undertaken in small groups.

- **The class can now do Exercise 11A from Pupil Book 1, or begin a problem of their own choice.**

Plenary

- Write some questions from one of the groups of students on the board.
- Prompt the other groups to add extra questions.
- Say that to finish off the lesson you are going to test out the questions on one or more individuals. Ask for volunteers to be interviewed.
- Use the questions written on the board as the basis of your test.
- Tell the class that their role is to decide, from the answers given, whether the volunteers agree with the statement or not.

Key Words

- survey
- questionnaire
- experiment
- statistics
- grouped data
- class interval
- tally
- frequency
- data-collection sheet
- database
- sample
- primary source
- secondary source
- data log
- two-way table
- discrete
- continuous

Homework

The homework could be used to complete the first stage of the problem as outlined in the lesson plan.

If time permits, the class could investigate a further problem from Exercise 11A or choose their own. Alternatively, they could work on the extension task.

Framework objectives – Stem-and-leaf diagrams

Calculate statistics, including with a calculator. Recognise when it is appropriate to use the range, mean and mode. Construct and use stem-and-leaf diagrams.

Oral and mental starter

- Using a counting stick, tell the students that, for example, the number 6 is at one end and 20 is at the other end. Ask them for the range. To vary the task, change the numbers, and introduce negatives, fractions and decimals.

- Write the numbers 1, 2, 2, 4, 4, 4, 4 on the board. Ask the class what the mode is, and how they found it. Repeat this procedure for the median and mean. Ask them which average they think best reflects the data. Obviously, it depends on what the data is about.
- Change the middle number to 3. Ask the class for the mode and median. Ask if the mean will go up, down or stay the same. This could be repeated several times, but at this stage keep the numbers in order.
- Now use the same numbers, but change the order. Ask them if changing the order makes any difference.
- Ask the class what happens to the mode, median, mean and range if each number is increased by one.
- Ask the class what happens to the mode, median, mean and range if the numbers are doubled.

Main lesson activity

- Tell the class that they are going to look at larger sets of data and a different way to present data sets so they are easy to analyse.
- Explain that it is quite straightforward to obtain a mode from a list of, say, seven numbers, but as the list becomes longer it is easier to make a mistake.
- Write on the board 31 numbers between 25 and 45, in random order, with some numbers repeated. Ask the students to sort them into the following groups: 20s, 30s and 40s. Then ask them to put these groups into numerical order on three separate lines in their books.
- Now, tell them that using a stem-and-leaf diagram reduces the amount of writing.
- Draw the stem on the board and ask one student to read out his/her numbers in order. Write the numbers on your diagram and let the class copy it into their books. Explain that it is important to line up the columns of numbers.

$$
\begin{array}{c|ccccc}
2 & 0 & 1 & 1 & 3 & \dots \\
3 & 1 & 1 & 2 & 4 & \dots \\
4 & 0 & 2 & 3 & 4 & \dots \\
\end{array}
$$

- Explain that to make sense the diagram will need a key. Use the first value for the key: for example, 2 | 0 represents 20.
- Ask them to use the diagram to write down the mode and the range.

- **The class can now do Exercise 11B from Pupil Book 1.**

Exercise 11B Answers

1 a 35 **b** 24 **c** 23
2 a 10 **b** 5 **c** 31
3 a 75 **b** 375

4 a
$$
\begin{array}{c|ccccccccc}
1 & 1 & 2 & 2 & 5 & 7 & 7 & 7 & 9 \\
2 & 2 & 3 & 3 & 3 & 3 & 4 & 5 & 6 \\
3 & 1 & 1 & 2 & 4 & 6 & 6 & 8 & 9 \\
4 & 2 & 5 & 7 & 7 & 8 & 9 \\
\end{array}
$$
Key: 1|2 represents 12 years old
b 23 **c** 38

1 Median = 24
2 Median = 19

Plenary

Key Words

- Show the class two stem-and-leaf diagrams using the same values, one set unordered and the other set ordered. For example:

```
2 | 0  2  5  6          2 | 5  6  0  2
3 | 1  1  2  6  7  9     3 | 7  1  1  9  6  2
4 | 1  4  6  7  7  7     4 | 7  7  6  1  7  4
```

- Ask the students to tell you what the difference is between the two diagrams.
- Follow up by asking them which is better. Prompt them to go for the ordered set of values.
- Tell the class that when creating a stem-and-leaf diagram, it is important to put the data into numerical order, as this will help them if they have to go on and, for example, find the mode or range.
- Reinforce the fact that the diagram needs to be presented neatly with the numbers aligned in columns, so that it is easy to see which is the longest row.

- range
- median
- mode
- modal class
- mean
- average
- stem-and-leaf diagram

Homework

1 Put the following sets of data into stem-and-leaf diagrams. Remember to give a key. In each case, write down the range and the mode.

a

22	45	36	32	32	33	27	42	41
37	29	31	34	30	44	42	29	30
44	32	25	26	32	29	41	22	32

b

72	91	83	77	92	92	84
83	70	77	87	95	77	94
91	78	85	93	77	78	87

c

3	14	25	36	6	31	22	27	8	4	4	26
21	25	4	25	32	5	4	27	23	23	28	33
38	4	30	10	31	11	29	34	4	34	24	29

Answers

1 a
```
2 | 2  2  5  6  7  9  9  9
3 | 0  0  1  2  2  2  2  3  4  6  7
4 | 1  1  2  2  4  4  5
```
Key: 2 | 2 represents 22   Range = 23, mode = 32

b
```
7 | 0  2  7  7  7  7  8  8
8 | 3  3  4  5  7  7
9 | 1  1  2  2  3  4  5
```
Key: 7 | 0 represents 70   Range = 25, mode = 77

c
```
0 | 3  4  4  4  4  4  4  5  6  8
1 | 0  1  4
2 | 1  2  3  3  4  5  5  5  6  7  7  8  9  9
3 | 0  1  1  2  3  4  4  6  8
```
Key: 0 | 3 represents 3   Range = 35, mode = 4

Framework objectives – Pie charts

Construct, on paper and using ICT:
 pie charts for categorical data;
 bar charts and frequency diagrams for discrete data.

Identify which are most useful in the context of the problem.

Oral and mental starter

- Write down 10, 20, 30, 40 and 50 on the board or on an OHT.
- Ask the class to give you three numbers that add up to 10. For example: 2, 5 and 3. Write the numbers on the board or the OHT (2 + 5 + 3 = 10).
- On the next line, write say 4, 10 and 6 (4 + 10 + 6 = 20).
- Ask the class to give you the third line (6 + 15 + 9 = 30).
- Repeat this with different sets of numbers.
- Now write on the board (or the OHT) three or four *even* numbers that add up to 20. For example: 2 + 6 + 8 + 4 = 20.
- Ask the class to scale the numbers down so that they add up to 10 (1 + 3 + 4 + 2 = 10).
- Now give the class multiples of three which add up to 30. For example: 12 + 6 + 9 + 3 = 30.
- Again ask the class to scale down the numbers so that they add up to 10 (4 + 2 + 3 + 1 = 10).
- Repeat this for different sets of numbers.

Main lesson activity

- Explain that in this lesson they will be drawing pie charts from data that has already been collected for them, and that this type of data is called **secondary data**. Tell the class that in a later lesson they will be using the data that they have collected for Lesson 11.1 to present pie charts of their own. Point out that this type of data is called **primary data**.
- Draw a circle on the board or on an OHT. Explain that the circles will have ten sectors. It may help the lesson to progress if the students are issued with a sheet containing circles on which the ten divisions are marked (see diagram).

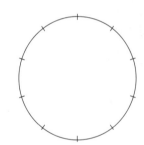

- Now present some quantities which add up to ten. Take, for example, the different types of cereal eaten regularly by ten students:

Cereal	Popcorn	Muesli	Corn flakes	Porridge
Number of students	2	3	4	1

- Ask the class to draw, on their sheets, a pie chart to represent this data, labelling the sectors clearly (see diagram).
- Now produce another table. For example, take the numbers of different types of house on a small estate:

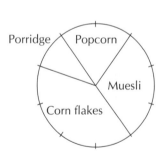

Type of house	Frequency	Number of sectors on pie chart
Terraced	8	
Bungalow	4	
Semi-detached	6	
Detached	2	
Total	20	10

Note that the total number of houses is 20 but there are only ten sectors on the pie chart. Prompt the class to tell you to scale down the frequencies, as in the oral and mental starter.

- Complete the table.

- Repeat this for several sets of frequencies but ensure that, at this stage, you use numbers which will easily scale down.
- Introduce questions which will require half a sector to be drawn.
- **The class can now do Exercise 11C from Pupil Book 1.**

1 Pie charts drawn with the angles as shown:

a

Subject	Maths	English	Science	Languages
Number of sections	4	2	3	1

b

Food	Cereal	Toast	Fruit	Cooked	None
Number of sections	3	2	$1\frac{1}{2}$	$2\frac{1}{2}$	1

c

Goals	0	1	2	3	4
Number of sections	1	2	3	$2\frac{1}{2}$	$1\frac{1}{2}$

d

Colour	Red	Green	Blue	Other
Number of sections	3	1	4	2

2 a 15 **b** 20 **c** 10 **d** 5

Key Words

- frequency diagram
- primary data
- secondary data
- bar chart
- bar-line graph
- pie chart
- sector
- scatter graph

Plenary

- Explain that the pie charts which they have been working on have all used total numbers (frequencies) that are multiples of ten to make the work easier.
- Warn the students that this will not always be the case. Eventually they will be required to draw pie charts which are not based on ten sectors.

Homework

Draw pie charts to represent the following data.

a The favourite TV programme of 30 adults

Subject	News	Soaps	Documentaries	Drama
Frequency	9	12	6	3

b The ages of 60 teachers in a school

Age (years)	21–30	31–40	41–50	51–60	Over 60
Frequency	12	18	18	9	3

c The favourite hobbies of 20 pupils

Hobby	Sport	Computing	Games console	Music	Other
Frequency	4	6	7	1	2

Answers
  a Number of sectors: News/3 Soaps/4 Documentaries/2 Drama/1
  b Number of sectors: 21–30/2 31–40/3 41–50/3 51–60/$1\frac{1}{2}$ Over 60/$\frac{1}{2}$
  c Number of sectors: Sport/2 Computing/3 Games console/$3\frac{1}{2}$ Music/$\frac{1}{2}$ Other/1

Framework objectives – Scatter graphs

Construct, on paper and using ICT, simple scatter graphs.

Oral and mental starter

● Copy this table on to the board or an OHT:

Favourite colour	Class 1	Class 2
Blue	9	15
Red	8	5
Yellow	5	6
Other	8	4

● Ask the class to tell you facts about the table. For example, blue is the favourite in both classes, three times as many like blue as red in Class 2, twice as many like 'other' in Class 1, etc.
● Change the numbers or the headings and repeat.
● Now ask them to draw a blank table the same size and with the same headings, and ask them to try to complete it with these facts (they may work in pairs or groups for this activity):
  • There are 30 pupils in each class.
  • In Class 1, 25 did not pick red.
  • In Class 1, no one picked yellow.
  • In Class 2, three times as many picked red as in Class 1.
  • 10 more picked blue than red in Class 1.
  • In Class 2, only three picked 'other'.
  • In Class 2, twice as many picked blue as yellow.
● Now ask how many picked yellow in Class 2. You may need to repeat the statements.

Answer:

Favourite colour	Class 1	Class 2
Blue	15	8
Red	5	15
Yellow	0	4
Other	10	3

Main lesson activity

● Tell the class that they are going to be looking at pairs of events to see whether there are any connections or relationships between them.
● Ask the class what happens to the height of children as they get older.
● Start to sketch a graph on the board, or on an OHT, of height against age and plot a cross near the origin. Tell the class that this cross represents a child who is very young.
● Now ask a student to come out to the board and plot a cross for a child who is one year older.
● Point out that the crosses need not be on a perfect straight line but that they show a trend or pattern.
● Tell the class that trend is called a **correlation**, and that in this case it is **positive correlation**.
● Now sketch, or have ready, a negative correlation graph.
● Tell the class that the axes represent the temperature and the sale of raincoats.
● Ask a student to identify a point that shows a hot day, and ask another what the raincoat sales were on that day.
● Now ask them what the trend or pattern tells them.
● Point out that this is a **negative correlation**.

● **The class can now do Exercise 11D from Pupil Book 1.**

Exercise 11D Answers

1 a Negative correlation: as price of tickets increases, number of tickets sold decreases
  b Positive correlation: as midday temperature increases, number of seaside visitors increases
2 Positive correlation: older pupils tend to spend more money
3 Negative correlation: more time spent watching TV means less time spent on homework
4 Negative correlation: value decreases with age
5 a 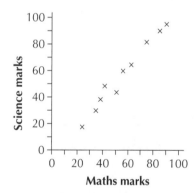   b Negative correlation: as people get older, they sleep fewer hours

Plenary

● Show the class graphs of positive, negative and no correlation in turn.
● Ask a student which one you are holding up.
● Prompt them again to tell you that positive correlation means that as one quantity increases, so does the other quantity.
● Also prompt them to tell you that negative correlation means that as one quantity increases, the other quantity decreases.
● If appropriate, ask them what no correlation means to them.

Homework

1 The scatter graph shows the test results of 10 pupils for Maths and Science. Describe what the graph tells you.

2 The table shows the cost of CDs in a record shop sale and the number sold in one day.

CD	A	B	C	D	E	F	G	H	I	J
Cost	£8	£12	£14	£10	£12	£9	£8	£10	£13	£12
Number sold	20	12	8	15	10	18	18	13	7	8

a Copy the graph and plot the points. The first two points have been done for you.

b Describe what the graph tells you.

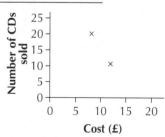

Answers
1 a Show positive correlation: Students who score high in Maths also score high in Science.
2 a Showing negative correlation
  b The higher the cost, the fewer CDs sold

LESSON
11.5

Framework objectives – Analysing data

Discuss a problem that can be addressed by statistical methods and identify related questions to explore.

Decide which data to collect to answer a question, and the degree of accuracy needed; identify possible sources.

Plan how to collect the data, including sample size; design and use two-way tables for discrete data.

Collect data using a suitable method, such as observation, controlled experiment using ICT, or questionnaire.

Communicate orally and on paper the results of a statistical enquiry and the methods used, using ICT as appropriate, justify the choice of what is presented

Oral and mental starter

- Write on the board or an OHT, 'Children eat more junk food than adults.'
- Tell the class to imagine that they have collected lots of data from children and adults to try to prove or disprove this statement.
- Tell them that you have gathered some facts and write these (below) on the board. Ask them what sort of diagrams they could use to show these facts.
  - 75% of the children and 45% of the adults surveyed eat junk food at least once a week.
  - The number of times that the children surveyed eat chips each week is as follows: 3, 3, 2, 4, 4, …
  - The approximate number of times people eat junk food each month is compared, in a table, with their ages. This yields two sets of data, one for children and one for adults.
- Prompt the class or lead them to suggest the use of bar charts and pie charts.
- You may wish to add to the list. Encourage them to give several choices for each one.
- Ask the class what data they could calculate from, for example, the number of times that the children surveyed eat chips.
- Prompt them to discuss averages and measures of spread.
- Write down key words for the class to copy into their books.

Main lesson activity

- Tell the class that the aim of this lesson is to write a brief report, stating whether or not they agree with a statement.
- Write on the board the planning stages for the report.
  - A statement, for example: 'Boys sleep longer than girls.'
  - A sentence saying what you think the data will tell you. For example: 'I think there is no difference.'
  - A bar chart, for example, showing, to nearest hour, for how long boys sleep each night.
  - One or more facts that you have found out from the bar chart. For example: most boys in this class sleep for 8 hours each night.
  - A pie chart, for example, showing data about the girls.
  - A sentence about the piece of data which occurs most often (the mode).
  - Possibly a stem-and-leaf diagram or scatter graph, and any other diagrams that you consider useful.
  - A brief conclusion about whether or not you agree with the statement.
- Tell the class *not* to do several of the same type of diagram, when they present their work but to use a variety of different methods.
- Tell them to give reasons why they have used each type of diagram.
- Stress that it is not wrong to disagree with the original statement.

- **The class can do Exercise 11E in Pupil Book 1 or the exercise can be used for a discussion about surveys, questionnaires and experiments. Alternatively, the class can analyse a set of data given to them or collected in Lesson 11.1 and write the final report.**

Note: In order for students to gain Level 5 in the SATs, they will have to express the sectors of a pie chart in degrees. Refer to Pupil Book 2 for examples and exercises.

Exercise 11E Answers

1 Survey
2 Data from books or Internet
3 Experiment
4 Survey
5 Questionnaire

6 Survey
7 Questionnaire
8 Questionnaire or survey
9 Survey
10 Experiment

SATs Answers

1 **a** 20, 40%
2 **a** $36°$ and $324°$ **b** Not possible to tell
3 **a** Frequency of $1 = 360° \div 20 = 18°$; Crime $= 54°$; Non-fiction $= 234°$, Fantasy $= 72°$
   b 1 pupil $= 165 \div 11 = 15°$; number of pupils $= 360 \div 15 = 24$
4 **a** The taller the horses, the heavier they are (positive correlation)
   b Approximately 590 kg   **c** Approximately 167 cm
   d Scatter graph with all points below the line that passes through (70, 70) and (110, 110)
5 **a** 65   **b** 30 and 50
   c Game A and Game B positive relationship; Game A and Game C no relationship
   d Game B and Game C no relationship

Plenary

- Have the checklist (see below), with an example, ready to give to the class at the end of the plenary.

Statement	A dice lands on 6 fewer times than on any other number
Sentence	I think that this will be incorrect as 6 has the same chance as any other number
Bar chart	Results recorded / Bar chart drawn
Facts	The results show that, although different numbers landed different numbers of times, they were almost the same
Other diagrams	None
Other facts	It landed on the number 4 the least number of times
Conclusion	If the dice is fair, it will land on 6 about the same number of times as on any other number

- Give the class the statement and ask for a comment. Try to prompt them to give you your sentence.
- Ask them how they could test this and write it up. Try to lead them through your checklist.
- Now give them the checklist to put in their books or to use as a guide for their reports.

Key Words
- **survey**
- **questionnaire**
- **experiment**
- **tally**
- **frequency**
- **data-collection sheet**
- **database**

Homework

The homework could be used to collect further data, but the main activity is to complete a written report using the data collected, in which the data is analysed and presented using the methods used in this chapter.

If extra time is available, investigate the time spent on homework compared with the time working on a problem in class. You could compare this for different subjects.

Number 4

Framework objectives – Fractions
Understand addition and subtraction of fractions.
(*This lesson covers the basis for addressing this objective*)

Oral and mental starter

Have a set of 'Follow me' cards (20 are suggested below) that test the simple cancelling of fractions.

1 START. You are $\frac{4}{8}$

2 I am $\frac{1}{2}$. You are $\frac{4}{14}$

3 I am $\frac{2}{7}$. You are $\frac{30}{40}$

4 I am $\frac{3}{4}$. You are $\frac{4}{18}$

5 I am $\frac{2}{9}$. You are $\frac{10}{12}$

6 I am $\frac{5}{6}$. You are $\frac{4}{12}$

7 I am $\frac{1}{3}$. You are $\frac{16}{18}$

8 I am $\frac{8}{9}$. You are $\frac{6}{20}$

9 I am $\frac{3}{10}$. You are $\frac{8}{20}$

10 I am $\frac{2}{5}$. You are $\frac{20}{32}$

11 I am $\frac{5}{8}$. You are $\frac{2}{8}$

12 I am $\frac{1}{4}$. You are $\frac{6}{10}$

13 I am $\frac{3}{5}$. You are $\frac{8}{18}$

14 I am $\frac{4}{9}$. You are $\frac{10}{15}$

15 I am $\frac{2}{3}$. You are $\frac{4}{40}$

16 I am $\frac{1}{10}$. You are $\frac{4}{20}$

17 I am $\frac{1}{5}$. You are $\frac{8}{10}$

18 I am $\frac{4}{5}$. You are $\frac{6}{14}$

19 I am $\frac{3}{7}$. You are $\frac{14}{16}$

20 I am $\frac{7}{8}$. END

Main lesson activity

- This is mainly a revision lesson on equivalent fractions and mixed numbers.
- Remind the students of methods for finding equivalent fractions. Give an example, such as $\frac{5}{6} = \frac{\square}{18}$ (multiply by 3).
- Refer back to the oral and mental starter if necessary.
- A list of tables may be helpful for weaker students.
- Now remind the students of the method used to convert fractions to mixed numbers. Give some examples, such as $\frac{24}{7} = 3\frac{3}{7}$, $\frac{11}{3} = 3\frac{2}{3}$, $\frac{14}{4} = 3\frac{2}{4} = 3\frac{1}{2}$.
- Now remind them of methods used to convert mixed numbers to fractions. Give some examples, such as $3\frac{3}{8} = \frac{27}{8}$, $2\frac{2}{5} = \frac{12}{5}$, $2\frac{7}{9} = \frac{25}{9}$.
- For those students who reach the extension work, cover how to find fractions of real quantities. Ask, 'What fraction of a kilogram is 3400 grams?' A kilogram is 1000 grams so the fraction is $\frac{3400}{1000}$, which converts to $3\frac{400}{1000}$ and cancels to $3\frac{2}{5}$.
- Show them what fraction of a metre 345 cm is (a metre is 100 cm, so the fraction is $\frac{345}{100}$, which converts to $3\frac{45}{100}$ and cancels to $3\frac{9}{20}$).

- **The class can now do Exercise 12A from Pupil Book 1**

1 a 15 **b** 18 **c** 75 **d** 24 **e** 28 **f** 36 **g** 24 **h** 21 **i** 12
2 a 23 **b** 36 **c** 24 **d** 52
3 a $1\frac{1}{2}$ **b** $1\frac{2}{5}$ **c** $1\frac{2}{7}$ **d** $2\frac{1}{8}$ **e** $7\frac{1}{2}$ **f** $3\frac{1}{7}$ **g** $2\frac{2}{15}$ **h** $3\frac{2}{5}$ **i** $2\frac{2}{5}$ **j** $2\frac{1}{6}$ **k** $2\frac{1}{4}$ **l** $4\frac{1}{10}$
4 a $\frac{5}{4}$ **b** $\frac{5}{2}$ **c** $\frac{19}{6}$ **d** $\frac{30}{7}$ **e** $\frac{41}{8}$ **f** $\frac{13}{5}$ **g** $\frac{15}{8}$ **h** $\frac{15}{4}$ **i** $\frac{17}{5}$ **j** $\frac{25}{11}$ **k** $\frac{37}{8}$ **l** $\frac{29}{9}$
5 a $1\frac{1}{6}$ **b** $1\frac{1}{3}$ **c** $1\frac{1}{7}$ **d** $1\frac{1}{4}$ **e** $1\frac{2}{5}$ **f** $1\frac{2}{5}$ **g** $1\frac{1}{6}$ **h** $2\frac{1}{6}$ **i** $1\frac{5}{6}$ **j** $3\frac{1}{5}$ **k** $1\frac{1}{2}$ **l** $2\frac{1}{7}$
6 a $2\frac{1}{3}$ **b** $2\frac{2}{7}$ **c** $2\frac{2}{5}$ **d** $4\frac{1}{2}$ **e** $2\frac{6}{7}$ **f** $4\frac{4}{5}$ **g** $4\frac{1}{3}$ **h** $2\frac{3}{8}$ **i** $12\frac{1}{6}$ **j** $7\frac{4}{5}$ **k** $4\frac{1}{3}$ **l** $11\frac{1}{3}$

a i $7\frac{3}{20}$ **ii** $2\frac{3}{10}$ **iii** $4\frac{1}{20}$ **iv** $5\frac{4}{5}$ **v** $1\frac{11}{20}$ **vi** $2\frac{1}{4}$
b i $2\frac{3}{10}$ **ii** $4\frac{1}{20}$ **iii** $7\frac{1}{2}$ **iv** $5\frac{3}{5}$ **v** $1\frac{9}{40}$ **vi** $6\frac{29}{50}$

Plenary

- Discuss the methods for converting improper fractions to mixed numbers.
- Discuss whether it is better to cancel before or after converting to a mixed number. For example, either $\frac{84}{9} = \frac{28}{3} = 9\frac{1}{3}$ or $\frac{84}{9} = 9\frac{3}{9} = 9\frac{1}{3}$
- Discuss converting top-heavy fractions to decimals (e.g., $\frac{13}{4} = 3\frac{1}{4} = 3.25$ and $\frac{19}{8} = 2\frac{3}{8} = 2.375$).
- Repeat with other examples if necessary.

Key Words

☐ **top-heavy fraction**
☐ **mixed number**
☐ **cancelling**
☐ **equivalent fraction**

Homework

1 Write these fractions as mixed numbers (cancel down if necessary):

a nine sixths **b** fourteen thirds **c** twelve sevenths **d** thirteen halves

e $\frac{22}{6}$ **f** $\frac{34}{7}$ **g** $\frac{31}{3}$ **h** $\frac{22}{8}$

2 Write these mixed numbers as top-heavy fractions:

a $2\frac{1}{7}$ **b** $3\frac{2}{5}$ **c** $1\frac{4}{9}$ **d** $2\frac{2}{3}$ **e** $3\frac{7}{10}$ **f** $4\frac{3}{5}$

Answers
1 a $1\frac{1}{2}$ **b** $4\frac{2}{3}$ **c** $1\frac{5}{7}$ **d** $6\frac{1}{2}$ **e** $3\frac{2}{3}$ **f** $4\frac{6}{7}$ **g** $10\frac{1}{3}$ **h** $2\frac{3}{4}$
2 a $\frac{15}{7}$ **b** $\frac{17}{5}$ **c** $\frac{13}{9}$ **d** $\frac{8}{3}$ **e** $\frac{37}{10}$ **f** $\frac{23}{5}$

LESSON
12.2

Framework objectives – Adding and subtracting fractions
Understand addition and subtraction of fractions.

Oral and mental starter

- Draw on the board or have already prepared on an OHT the diagram shown.
- Explain the 'key', which indicates the values to subtract in each direction.
- Point to various cells and ask students to give you the value of the cell.
- These could be asked for in order or the cells could be picked at random.
- Other diagrams and 'keys' are:

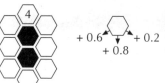

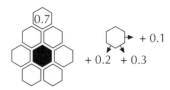

Main lesson activity

- Write the following problem on the board: $\frac{1}{2} + \frac{1}{3}$.
- Ask the pupils to think of the answer, or write it down. The majority will give $\frac{2}{5}$.
- Get the correct answer and discuss the processes used to add fractions with a different denominator.
- Students have met this before and should recall the need to use the same denominator.
- Work through the original example in some detail: $\frac{1}{2} + \frac{1}{3} = \frac{3}{6} + \frac{2}{6} = \frac{5}{6}$.
- Repeat with $\frac{3}{8} + \frac{5}{12} = \frac{9}{24} + \frac{10}{24} = \frac{19}{24}$, and $\frac{4}{5} + \frac{3}{4} = \frac{16}{20} + \frac{15}{20} = \frac{31}{20} = 1\frac{11}{20}$.
- Recall the need to write top-heavy fractions as mixed numbers.
- Now ask for the answer to $\frac{2}{3} - \frac{1}{4} = \frac{8}{12} - \frac{3}{12} = \frac{5}{12}$.
- The method is basically the same, but with the top two numbers subtracted rather than added.
- Repeat with $\frac{4}{5} - \frac{2}{3} = \frac{12}{15} - \frac{10}{15} = \frac{2}{15}$, and $\frac{5}{12} - \frac{3}{8} = \frac{10}{24} - \frac{9}{24} = \frac{1}{24}$.
- Now ask for the answer to $\frac{4}{5}$ of 45.
- Recall the method for this, to find $\frac{1}{5}$ of 45 (= 9) and then multiply by 4 (= 36).
- Repeat with $\frac{3}{4}$ of £28 (= £21), $\frac{2}{7}$ of 35 kg (= 10 kg).
- Ask for the answers to $3 \times \frac{4}{7} (= \frac{12}{7} = 1\frac{5}{7})$ and $5 \times \frac{4}{5} (= \frac{20}{5} = 4)$.
- Ask for the answers to $\frac{3}{4} \div 3 (= \frac{3}{12} = \frac{1}{4})$ and $\frac{2}{7} \div 5 (= \frac{2}{35})$.

- **The class can now do Exercise 12B from Pupil Book 1.**

1 a 12 b 30 c 15 d 6 e 20 f 4 g 18 h 12

2 a $\frac{11}{12}$ b $\frac{17}{30}$ c $\frac{11}{15}$ d $\frac{5}{6}$ e $\frac{9}{20}$ f $\frac{3}{4}$ g $\frac{17}{18}$ h $\frac{5}{12}$

3 a $\frac{1}{12}$ b $\frac{7}{30}$ c $\frac{1}{15}$ d $\frac{1}{6}$ e $\frac{3}{20}$ f $\frac{1}{4}$ g $\frac{13}{18}$ h $\frac{1}{12}$

4 a $\frac{7}{12}$ b $\frac{1}{2}$ c $\frac{11}{20}$ d $\frac{23}{24}$ e $\frac{17}{30}$ f $1\frac{17}{24}$ g $\frac{5}{6}$ h $1\frac{7}{12}$ i $\frac{13}{24}$ j $\frac{1}{2}$ k $\frac{1}{20}$ l $\frac{13}{18}$ m $\frac{1}{6}$

n $\frac{1}{24}$ o $\frac{1}{3}$ p $\frac{7}{12}$

1 a $\frac{1}{8}+\frac{1}{4}$ b $\frac{1}{2}+\frac{1}{4}$ c $\frac{1}{2}+\frac{1}{12}$ d $\frac{1}{2}+\frac{1}{6}$

2 a $\frac{1}{2}+\frac{1}{4}+\frac{1}{8}$ b $\frac{1}{2}+\frac{1}{6}+\frac{1}{6}$ c $\frac{1}{4}+\frac{1}{4}+\frac{1}{8}$ d $\frac{1}{2}+\frac{1}{3}+\frac{1}{8}$

Plenary

- Write some fractions on the board, including some mixed numbers (e.g., $\frac{1}{7}$, $\frac{3}{8}$, $\frac{3}{14}$, $\frac{5}{6}$, $2\frac{1}{3}$, $1\frac{2}{5}$).
- Ask the students to add and subtract combinations of these.
- Make sure they are aware of the need to convert mixed numbers to top-heavy fractions or to do the integer part separately.

Key Words

- lowest common denominator
- top-heavy fractions
- mixed number

Homework

1 Convert each of the following fractions to equivalent fractions with a common denominator, and then work out the answer, cancelling down or writing as a mixed number, as appropriate:

a $\frac{1}{3}+\frac{1}{2}$ b $\frac{1}{7}+\frac{1}{4}$ c $\frac{3}{5}+\frac{3}{4}$ d $\frac{4}{15}+\frac{3}{5}$ e $\frac{3}{8}+\frac{1}{6}$ f $\frac{5}{12}+\frac{3}{4}$ g $\frac{1}{2}-\frac{1}{3}$

h $\frac{5}{7}-\frac{1}{3}$ i $\frac{3}{5}-\frac{1}{4}$

Answers

1 a $\frac{5}{6}$ b $\frac{11}{28}$ c $1\frac{7}{20}$ d $\frac{13}{15}$ e $\frac{13}{24}$ f $1\frac{1}{6}$ g $\frac{1}{6}$ h $\frac{8}{21}$ i $\frac{7}{20}$

Framework objectives – BODMAS

Use the order of operations, including brackets with more complex calculations.

Oral and mental starter

- Write the following operations on the board:

  $+ 5$ ⟩ $\times 2$ ⟩ $- 4$ ⟩ $\div 2$ ⟩

- Ask the students to arrange the operations in any order.
- Ask them to pick a number and work through the operations in the order they have chosen, then subtract the number they thought of. For example, the order as above, starting with 7, gives:

  $7 \rightarrow 12 \rightarrow 24 \rightarrow 20 \rightarrow 10 \rightarrow 3$

  (Note: there are 24 possible arrangements, but only seven answers: –3, –1.5, 0.5, 1, 2, 3, 6.)
- Discuss whether the order matters. In the above example, the answers of 1 all have ÷ 2 and × 2 as consecutive operations.
- Remind the students of the mathematical rule for the order of operations in a calculation.
- Students should recall BODMAS, which is the focus of the main lesson.

Main lesson activity

- This is a revision lesson on BODMAS.
- Recall the meaning of BODMAS and discuss what it implies.
- Emphasise the important rules, and that addition and subtraction are of equal worth if there are no other operations in the calculation; the same is true for multiplication and division. For these calculations work from left to right.
- Do some examples, in which you demonstrate the order of operation:

  $4 \times 2^2 - 12 \div 4$

Firstly, work out the power	$4 \times 4 - 12 \div 4$
Secondly, the division and the multiplication	$16 - 3$
Finally, the subtraction	13

  $(5 + 4)^2 \times 4 \div 6$

Firstly, work out the bracket	$9^2 \times 4 \div 6$
Secondly, the power	$81 \times 4 \div 6$
Thirdly, the multiplication	$324 \div 6$
Finally, the division	54

  Point out that the order in the last two steps is decided by working from left to right.

- **The class can now do Exercise 12C from Pupil Book 1.**

1 **a** 33 **b** 16 **c** 51 **d** 2 **e** 63 **f** 4 **g** 63 **h** 8 **i** 5 **j** 16 **k** 4 **l** 12
2 **a** 23 **b** 67 **c** 28 **d** 192 **e** 7 **f** 57 **g** 74 **h** 76 **i** 10 **j** 5 **k** 5 **l** 5
  m −4.7 **n** 6
3 **a** $3 \times (7 + 1) = 24$ **b** $(3 + 7) \times 2 = 20$ **c** $2 \times (3 + 1) \times 4 = 32$ **d** $(2 + 3)^2 = 25$
  e $5 \times 5 + (5 \div 5) = 26$ **f** $5 \times (5 + 5) \div 5 = 10$ **g** $(5 \times 5 + 5) \div 5 = 6$
  h $(15 - 3)^2 = 144$

Extension Answers

a $4 \times 6 + (4 - 3) \times 8 + 1 = 33$ or $4 \times 6 + (4 - 3) \times (8 + 1)$
b $4 \times (6 + 4) - 3 \times 8 + 1 = 17$
c $4 \times (6 + 4 - 3) \times (8 + 1) = 252$
d $4 \times 6 + 4 - 3 \times (8 + 1)$

Plenary

Key Words

- Ask the class 'Which operation comes first: multiplication or division? What about addition or subtraction?' Make sure they understand that neither operation takes precedence within these pairs, but when there is a choice between them they must work from left to right.
- Write a complex calculation on the board, such as:
  $(5^2 - 2) \times 4 + (8 - 6) \div (2^2 \div 16)$
- Discuss the order of operations and evaluate the above in order (or ask students if they can do it):

- order of operations
- power
- brackets

Firstly, the powers inside brackets	$(25 - 2) \times 4 + (8 - 6) \div (4 \div 16)$
Secondly, each bracket	$23 \times 4 + 2 \div \frac{1}{4}$
Thirdly, multiplication and division	$92 + 8$
Finally, the addition	100

Homework

1 Write the operation that you do first in each of these calculations, and then work out each one:

  a $6 + 2 \times 3$ **b** $(6 + 2) \times 3$ **c** $6 \times 7 - 5$ **d** $6 \times (7 - 5)$

2 Work out the following, showing each step of the calculation:

  a $32 \div 4 + 4^2$ **b** $32 \div (4 + 4)^2$ **c** $2 \times 3 + 2^2$ **d** $2 \times (3 + 2)^2$

  e $\dfrac{100}{2 \times 4}$ **f** $\dfrac{90 - 30}{3 \times 5}$ **g** $\sqrt{(13^2 - 5^2)}$ **h** $\dfrac{(3 + 3)^2}{3 - 1}$

3 Write out each of the following with brackets to make the calculation true:

  a $2 \times 9 - 1 = 16$ **b** $5 + 3 \times 2 = 16$ **c** $2 + 3 \times 1 + 4 = 25$

Answers
  1 **a** 12 **b** 24 **c** 37 **d** 12
  2 **a** 24 **b** 0.5 **c** 10 **d** 50 **e** 12.5 **f** 4 **g** 12 **h** 18
  3 **a** $2 \times (9 - 1) = 16$ **b** $(5 + 3) \times 2 = 16$ **c** $(2 + 3) \times (1 + 4) = 25$

Framework objectives – Multiplying decimals

Use standard column procedures for multiplication of integers and decimals, including by decimals such as 0.6 or 0.06; understand where to position the decimal point by considering equivalent calculations.

Oral and mental starter

- Ask the students to think of an odd number and an even number, and then add them together. Ask them if the result is odd or even, and if this is always true.
- Repeat with two odd numbers and two even numbers.
- Repeat with subtraction rather than addition.
- Repeat with multiplication rather than addition.
- Repeat with squaring an odd number and squaring an even number.

Main lesson activity

- This is a lesson on multiplying decimals.
- Students will need calculators for this activity.
- Put a variety of problems on board such as 0.5×0.3, 0.4×0.6, 0.7×0.4, etc.
- Ask the class to work out the answers on their calculators. Write these on the board.
- Ask them if they can see the rule for calculations such as 0.3×0.5. Establish that there is always the same number of decimal places in the calculation as in the answer. Therefore, since $3 \times 5 = 15$, and there must be two decimal places in the answer ($0._{\_} \times 0._{\_} = 0._{\_\_}$), $0.3 \times 0.5 = 0.15$.
- Work through some more examples (without a calculator), such as 0.4×0.3 ($= 0.12$), 0.5×0.2 ($= 0.10$).
  Point out that the answer to the latter example would normally be written as 0.1.
- Now ask the class to work out the answers to the following on their calculators: 20×0.7, 30×0.4, 50×0.6.
- Ask the students if they can see the rule for calculations such as 20×0.4. Show them how to rewrite this as an equivalent calculation which is easier to work out:

    $20 \times 0.4 = 2 \times 4 = 8$.

  Establish the principle that when working with products, we can multiply one number by 10, whilst dividing the other by 10 to compensate.
- Work through some more examples (without a calculator), such as 30×0.7 ($= 3 \times 7 = 21$), 40×0.8 ($= 4 \times 8 = 32$).
- If possible extend the ideas to problems with more decimal places, such as 0.02×0.3, 0.004×0.03, 400×0.6, 300×0.07.

- **The class can now do Exercise 12D from Pupil Book 1.**

Plenary

- This plenary relates to the oral and mental starter.
- Introduce the idea of a counter example, that is, if someone says 'All square numbers are even', a counter example is $3^2 = 9$.
- Ask for counter examples to the following statements:
    All numbers have an even number of factors;
    $a^2 = 2a$; $(a + b)^2 = a^2 + b^2$;
    All multiples of 3 are odd;
    All multiples of 9 under 100 have digits that add up to 9;
    All prime numbers are odd;
    Numbers in the 7 times table do not end in 5.

Homework

1 Without using a calculator, write down the answer to:

   a 0.5×0.7 b 0.5×0.2 c 0.8×0.8 d 0.9×0.3

   e 0.3×0.5 f 0.6×0.8 g 0.7×0.2 h 0.5×0.5

2 Without using a calculator, work out:

   a 20×0.6 b 0.7×30 c 0.4×40 d 0.3×70

   e 0.2×60 f 0.3×80 g 0.6×80 h 0.4×70

Answers
1 a 0.35 b 0.1 c 0.64 d 0.27 e 0.15 f 0.48 g 0.14 h 0.25
2 a 12 b 21 c 16 d 21 e 12 f 24 g 48 h 28

LESSON 12.5

Framework objectives – Dividing decimals

Use standard column procedures for division of integers and decimals, including by decimals such as 0.6 or 0.06; understand where to position the decimal point by considering equivalent calculations.

Oral and mental starter

- Ask students to draw a 5 × 5 grid.
- They can then fill in the spaces with 25 numbers from 3 to 41 (but not 30 or 40).
- The numbers can go in any order and should not have any repeats.
- Now throw three dice.

41	16	6	15	23
32	27	29	25	34
21	3	31	38	7
19	35	18	9	26
12	13	37	14	39

- The first dice is the whole-number part of the mixed number.
- The other two give the fraction part (the larger value is the denominator, and the smaller number is the numerator). If these are same, throw these again. Do not cancel down mixed numbers, such as $2\frac{4}{6}$.
- Students have to work out the numerator of the mixed number (e.g., 16) and then cross this off on their grid.
- The first student to cross-off five in a row 'wins'.

Main lesson activity

- This is a lesson on dividing integers and decimals
- The students will need calculators.
- Ask the class to write down, and then work out using their calculators, the answers to problems such as 0.6 ÷ 0.2, 0.8 ÷ 0.4, 0.36 ÷ 0.2.
- Write their answers on the board and ask if they can see rules for calculations such as 0.6 ÷ 0.2. Show them how to rewrite this as an equivalent calculation:
    0.6 ÷ 0.2 = 6 ÷ 2 = 3.
  Establish the principle that the numbers in the division can both be multiplied by 10 without affecting the answer. This is done repeatedly until the divisor is a whole-number, which makes the calculation straightforward.
- Work through some similar examples (without a calculator), such as 0.4 ÷ 0.1 (= 4 ÷ 1 = 4), 0.45 ÷ 0.3 (= 4.5 ÷ 3 = 1.5).
- Repeat for calculations such as 30 ÷ 0.5, 42 ÷ 0.6, 200 ÷ 0.4.
  Demonstrate that the same method of using equivalent calculations to rewrite with a whole-number divisor applies (60 ÷ 0.3 = 600 ÷ 3 = 200).
- Repeat with 500 ÷ 0.2 (= 5000 ÷ 2 = 250)
- Repeat with 400 ÷ 0.4 (= 4000 ÷ 4 = 1000)
- If possible cover some problems such as 0.8 ÷ 0.04, 50 ÷ 0.02, 0.6 ÷ 0.002, 300 ÷ 0.006, etc. It may be best to leave this until students have worked through Questions 1 and 2.

- **The class can now do Exercise 12E from Pupil Book 1.**

Exercise 12E Answers

1 a 2 b 3 c 6 d 3 e 2 f 4 g 0.6 h 0.4 i 0.8 j 4 k 8 l 0.3
  m 1 n 1 o 1 p 4
2 a 500 b 1500 c 50 d 1000 e 300 f 100 g 500 h 2000 i 600
  j 800 k 4000 l 2000 m 60 n 100 o 120 p 1000
3 a 20 b 0.6 c 30 d 20 e 3 f 0.3
4 a 500 b 10 000 c 8000 d 20 000 e 1200 r 200 000
5 20 000

Extension Answers

1 a 156.4 b 15.64 c 460 d 460
2 a 0.1824 b 18240 c 1824 d 0.1824
3 a 1540 b 2.8 c 550 d 154

SATs Answers

1 a 21 b 1980 c 1995
2 a 64, 864, 675 b 2520, 15
3 a 91.44 m b 109.36 yards

Plenary

- This plenary covers both multiplication and division of decimals.
- Ask students to give a number that makes 0.8 smaller when multiplied by it.
- Obtain some examples and write them on the board. What is the common characteristic?
- Establish that any value less than 1 does this.
- What about a value that makes 0.8 larger when multiplied by it?
- Obtain some examples and write them on the board. What is the common characteristic?
- Establish that any value larger than 1 will work.
- Repeat the above procedures with 0.8 divided by a number.
- Establish that values greater than 1 make 0.8 smaller and values less than 1 make 0.8 larger.
- If time is available, test the students' understanding by asking for missing values in:
  $0.8 \times \ldots = 8$, $0.8 \div \ldots = 0.08$, $0.8 \times \ldots = 0.08$, $0.8 \div \ldots = 8$

Key Words
- ☐ equivalent calculation
- ☐ decimal place

Homework

1 Without using a calculator, work out:

  a $0.6 \div 0.3$ b $0.8 \div 0.2$ c $0.8 \div 0.1$ d $0.4 \div 0.2$

  e $0.5 \div 0.1$ f $0.8 \div 0.4$ g $0.9 \div 0.3$ h $0.12 \div 0.3$

2 Without using a calculator, work out:

  a $60 \div 0.6$ b $80 \div 0.2$ c $80 \div 0.8$ d $60 \div 0.2$

  e $90 \div 0.3$ f $20 \div 0.4$ g $60 \div 0.1$ h $90 \div 0.2$

Answers

  1 a 2 b 4 c 8 d 2 e 5 f 2 g 3 h 0.4
  2 a 100 b 400 c 100 d 300 e 300 f 50 g 600 h 450

Algebra 5

Framework objectives – Expansion of brackets

Multiply a single term over a bracket.

Oral and mental starter

- Tell the class the following story.
- Some prisoners are trying to find their way through a maze of connected cubes inside a larger cube. Each cube is connected to six others by a door in each face. Each door has a number written on it. If a door's number has a prime number of factors, the door leads to a safe room, otherwise it is booby trapped.
- Ask the class if door 24 leads to a safe room.
- You will need to lead the class through the process of finding pairs of factors, such as 1, 24 and 2,12, until they see eight factors. This means that the room is booby trapped, as 8 is not a prime number.
- What about door 64? Ask them if this is safe? (Seven factors, a prime number, so the door leads to safety.)
- The six doors leading from one room are numbered 84, 77, 25, 36, 100 and 160. How many doors are safe and which are they?
- The correct answer is only one, door 25, as it has three factors.
- You may wish to take the puzzle further by showing the class that all safe doors have square numbers on them, as these will have an odd number of factors. However, more thought will be needed as to which of the square numbers are safe.

Main lesson activity

- Write on the board $4(2 + 7)$, and ask the class what number this will give when calculated (36).
- Discuss with the class the notion of multiplying by 4 over the whole of the bracket.
- Discuss also how different students may have done the calculation. Some may have added the 2 and 7 to calculate $4 \times 9 = 36$. Others may have multiplied by 4 each term in the brackets, which gives $8 + 28 = 36$.
- Make sure that each and every student can see that the same answer is found whichever way the calculation is made.
- Repeat this for a bracket containing a subtraction: for example, $3(8 - 6)$.
- Get the class to show that both methods give the same answer. That is:
$$3(8 - 6) = 3 \times 2 = 6$$
$$3(8 - 6) = 3 \times 8 + 3 \times (-6)$$
$$= 3 \times 8 - 3 \times 6$$
$$= 24 - 18 = 6$$
- Now write on the board $3(5 + 4b)$ and ask the class how they would multiply the 3 over the whole of the bracket. Explain that this is called **expansion**.
- Show that this expands to $15 + 12b$.
- Give another example:
$$2(6p - 3)$$
$$= 2 \times 6p + 2 \times (-3)$$
$$= 2 \times 6p - 2 \times 3$$
$$= 12p - 6$$
- **The class can now do Exercise 13A from Pupil Book 1.**

1 a 18, 10, 18 **b** 9, 27, 6, 21, 27, 3, 2, 3, 7 **c** 5, 7, 35, 4, 3, 20, 15, 35, 5, 4, 5, 3
d 4, 7, 28, 4, 5, 4, 2, 20, 8, 28, $4 \times 5 + 4 \times 2$
2 a $6 + 3t$ **b** $5m + 20$ **c** $12 - 4k$ **d** $2w - 8$ **e** 4, 3, k, $12 + 3k$
f 5, q, 2, $5q + 10$ **g** 4, 5, 4, $-t$, $20 - 4t$ **h** 2, n, 2, -3, $2n - 6$
3 a $12 + 3k$ **b** $5m + 35$ **c** $12 + 4t$ **d** $10 - 2n$ **e** $3w - 6$ **f** $6h - 12$
g $15 + 5g$ **h** $2f - 14$ **i** $3 - 3q$
4 a 12 **b** $15 + 10t$ **c** $3w$, -2, $12w - 8$ **d** 5, $4k$, $10 + 8k$ **e** 3, $5d$, 3, 2, $15d + 6$
f 5, 4, 5, $-3q$, $20 - 15q$ **g** 4, $2n$, 4, 7, $8n + 28$
5 a $6a + 9$ **b** $8 - 6k$ **c** $5 + 15p$ **d** $8q - 12$ **e** $12 + 6t$ **f** $28 + 21m$
g $10y - 6$ **h** $12 - 8n$ **i** $10m + 20$ **j** $9p - 6$ **k** $30 + 18y$ **l** $6k - 8$

1 Each row, each column and each diagonal should be shown to add up to $3x$

Plenary

Key Words

- Ask the class if anyone can describe like terms.
- Write $5m$ on the board. Ask for like terms to $5m$. Write a few of these on the board.
- Ask: 'What can we do with these like terms? Can we add them? Can we subtract them?' Invite the class to give some examples of these two operations
- Now ask for some unlike terms. Repeat the two questions, the answer to both of which is 'No'.

- [ ] **expression**
- [ ] **expand**
- [ ] **simplify**

Homework

1 Expand each of the the following.

a $2(3a + 4b)$ **b** $3(5t - 2k)$ **c** $6(n + 2p)$ **d** $5(2q - p)$

e $4(7 + w)$ **f** $2(5 + 2m)$ **g** $5(3y - t)$ **h** $7(2x - 3n)$

2 Find the area of each of the rectangles below.

a

	m	5
4		

b

	4	$3m$
3		

c

	$5k$	$3t$
5		

Answers

1 a $6a + 8b$ **b** $15t - 6k$ **c** $6n + 12p$ **d** $10q - 5p$ **e** $28 + 4w$ **f** $10 + 4m$ **g** $15y - 5t$ **h** $14x - 21n$
2 a $4m + 20$ **b** $12 + 9m$ **c** $10k + 15t$

Framework objectives – Solving equations
Solve linear equations with integer coefficients.

Oral and mental starter

- Draw on the board the circles shown on the right.
- Tell the class that the numbers in each circle follow the same rule. Can they work out the missing number in the third circle?
- If necessary, offer a hint: 'Differences'.
- Eventually, someone will give the correct answer, either as a guess or because he/she has worked it out. Get the student to tell you (quietly) whether they know how to work it out. Then put the correct answer (3) into the space.
- Ask this student to give another circle with a number missing from the lower right-hand sector. The rest of the class has to try to find the missing number.
- If all, or some, of the class are struggling, go through the differences between the numbers and ask if they notice any special numbers. Hopefully, they will recognise that the difference between the top number and the lower left-hand number is a square number in each case. The lower right-hand number is the square root of this difference.
- For those who find the rule quickly, the problem can be extended to involve cube roots.

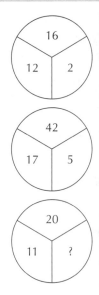

Main lesson activity

- Write the equation $3x = 15$ on the board, and ask the class to solve it. Remind them that to solve an equation they first have to find the inverse mapping, from which the unknown value can be found.
- When you are given the answer $x = 5$ (do not accept 5 on its own), ask how this value was found.

    Inverse mapping would give:

    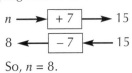

- So, you are looking for the response: 'Divide both sides by 3'.
- Write on the board the equation $n + 7 = 15$. Then go through the inverse mapping routine to obtain:

    $$n \longrightarrow \boxed{+\,7} \longrightarrow 15$$
    $$8 \longleftarrow \boxed{-\,7} \longleftarrow 15$$

    So, $n = 8$.

- If the students start to see short routes to the answers, this should be encouraged, but ensure that they know why these work. (A learnt trick, with no understanding, is easily forgotten.)
- Write another equation on the board, $4t - 3 = 17$, and ask the class how to solve it.
- Go through this with the whole class, using their suggestions:

    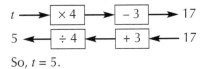

    So, $t = 5$.

- **The class can now do Exercise 13B from Pupil Book 1.**

Plenary

- Ensure that all the students have grasped the technique of applying inverse mapping to solve equations by working through, with their active participation, some more examples.
- Next, discuss with the class how to solve equations containing brackets.
- Is it easier first to expand the brackets, then solve? Or is it easier first, to divide both sides?
- Might it depend on what numbers are involved? If so, what might be special about the numbers to suggest one way or the other would be better?
- There is no need to do more than raise the questions to challenge the students, get them thinking and prepare them for their homework.

Key Words

☐ solve
☐ variable
☐ unknown
☐ inverse mapping

Homework

1 Solve the following equations:

   a $4x = 16$ **b** $3x = 30$ **c** $2m = 18$ **d** $5n = 35$

2 Solve the following equations:

   a $6n + 1 = 19$ **b** $4x - 3 = 21$ **c** $2m + 3 = 11$ **d** $9x - 2 = 25$

3 Solve the following equations:

   a $4(3t + 1) = 28$ **b** $3(4m + 5) = 39$ **c** $4(5m + 3) = 72$ **d** $5(2k + 3) = 65$

   e $3(3t - 5) = 12$ **f** $5(2x - 3) = 30$ **g** $4(2t - 5) = 36$ **h** $3(5x - 4) = 18$

LESSON 13.3

Framework objectives – Constructing equations to solve

Construct and solve linear equations with integer coefficients (unknown on either or both sides, without and with brackets) using appropriate methods (e.g., inverse operations, transforming both sides in same way).

Oral and mental starter

- Tell the class that you are going to give them a number, to which you are going to apply a rule and give them the answer, but not the rule.
- Then ask the class to work out the rule from those two numbers.
- Choose a simple rule such as × 2 + 1, and a not too large starting number.
- When they have found the rule, move on to other starting numbers and rules.

Main lesson activity

- Draw on the board Jim and Jim's grandad.
- Write down that grandad is four times older than Jim.
- Their ages add up to 105. What are their ages?
- When the class starts to suggest ages, stop them.
- Tell them they are to find the solution by using algebra.
- To solve this problem, start by letting Jim's age be m, say, and then work out Grandad's age in terms of m. Lead the students to $4m$, and away from trying to simply choose another letter.

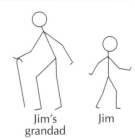

Jim's grandad   Jim

- Given their ages add up to 105, ask if anyone can give an equation to describe the situation.
- Help the class to see that $m + 4m = 105$, and hence $5m = 105$.
- This gives $m = 21$. So, what are their ages? (21 years and $4 \times 21 = 84$ years.)
- After this, give the class another problem.
- 'I think of a number, multiply it by five, add seven to the result and get 22. What is my number?
- Let the starting number be n.
- Multiplying it by 5 gives $5n$. Adding 7 gives $5n + 7$. Here the class should be involved to work out these – possibly calling individual students to the board.
- Set up the question: $5n + 7 = 22$. Again, get the students involved.
- Apply the inverse mapping routine to obtain $n = 3$.

- **The class can now do Exercise 13C from Pupil Book 1.**

Plenary

Key Words

- Tell each student to think of a number, which they must not tell anyone.
- Double that number. Then add on 10.
- Halve the answer, take away the number first thought of.
- Write on the board 5, which is the number they should all have.
- Tell the class that they can make up little tricks up using algebra. Show how this is done:

Think of a number	n
Double the number	$2n$
Add on 10	$2n + 10$
Halve the answer	$n + 5$
Take away the first number	5

- Ask the class to make up their own trick and try it out.

☐ **equation**
☐ **expression**

Homework

1 Grandma is seven times as old as her grandson is now. If their ages add up to 96, how old is Grandma?

2 The sum of two consecutive odd numbers is 152. Find the numbers.

3 Mark weighs 7 kg more than his brother. Their total weight is 71 kg. How much does Mark weigh?

4 Phoebe's Auntie Ann is three times as old as Phoebe. The sum of their ages is 52. Find their ages.

5 I think of a number, add 8 to it, double the answer, subtract 10 and I end up with 16.

   i If the number I first thought of was n, write down an equation that involves n and 16.

   i Solve the equation to find the number I first thought of.

Answers
1 84 years
2 75 and 77
3 39 kg
4 13 and 39 years
5 i $2n + 6 = 16$ ii 5

Framework objectives – Lines and equations
Plot the graphs of linear functions, where y is given explicitly in terms of x.

Oral and mental starter

- Ask the class if anyone can tell you how many factors 8 has. The answer is four (1, 2, 4, 8).
- Now ask them how many factors 28 has. The answer is six (1, 2, 4, 7, 14, 28).
- Next, ask if they think 128 has more or fewer factors than 28. It has more, but how many? It has eight altogether (1, 2, 4, 8, 16, 32, 64, 128).
- Then set them a challenge: 'Which three-digit number has the most factors?'
- They could work together in groups of two or three on this problem.
- Do encourage them to start from the factors. That is, what numbers have the factors 1, 2, 3, 4, 5, 6, 7, …?
- The correct answer is 840 with 32 factors (1, 2, 3, 4, 5, 6, 7, 8, 10, 12, 14, 15, 20, 21, 24, 28 and their respective partners.)

Main lesson activity

- Draw a grid on the board with both axes graduated from 0 to 6. Then draw the dashed line $y = 4$, and put small crosses on the integer coordinates along that line.
- Ask the class 'What are the coordinates of the points on the dashed line?'
- Write the correct answers on the board in a list as they are given . (It is better if they do not come in order.)
- Then ask 'What do you notice about the coordinates?'
- The answer you want is that the second number is always a 4. You will need to tell them that this is the y-ordinate and so y is always equal to 4. This means that the line represents the equation $y = 4$.
- Repeat the above for the line $x = 2$.

- **The class can now do Questions 1 to 3 from Exercise 13D, Pupil Book 1.**

- Before most students start Question 4, you may wish to go through a similar example with them.
- Draw on the board a grid with x from 0 to 3 and y from 0 to 6. On this draw the dashed line $y = x + 3$. Mark on the coordinates (0, 3), (1, 4), (2, 5) and (3, 6). Ask the class what the coordinates of these points are. Put their answers on the board in a list. It is helpful if they are put in order.
- Ask if they can spot any connections between the first number and the second number. You may need to go back to the mapping ideas as
    $0 \rightarrow 3 \quad 1 \rightarrow 4 \quad 2 \rightarrow 5 \quad 3 \rightarrow 6$
- Do not tell them the answer. Just keep giving some hints until someone says: 'It's add 3'. Then get them to give you the equation $y = x + 3$.

- **The class can now do Question 4 from Exercise 13D, Pupil Book 1.**

Exercise 13D Answers

1 a (0, 1), (1, 1), (2, 1), (3, 1), (4, 1), (5, 1); $y = 1$
  b (3, 0), (3, 1), (3, 2), (3, 3), (3, 4), (3, 5), (3, 6), (3, 7); $x = 3$
  c (0, 5), (1, 5), (2, 5), (3, 5), (4, 5), (5, 5); $y = 5$
3 a (1, 3) **b** (2, 4) **c** (5, 1)
  d The x-ordinates are the same, and so are the y-ordinates. **e** (17, 28)
4 a $y = x$ **b** $y = x + 1$ **c** $y = x + 2$ **d** $y = 2x$ **e** $y = 3x$ **f** $x + y = 4$

Extension Answers

1 a (0, 1), (1, 3), (2, 5), (3, 7)
  c i (0, 3), (1, 5), (2, 7), (3, 9) **ii** (0, 5), (1, 7), (2, 9), (3, 11)
    iii (0, 4), (1, 6), (2, 8), (3, 10)

Plenary

- Put on the board a simple grid with a cross at the coordinates (5, 2).
- Ask the class for two straight lines which pass through this point, giving their equations. You are looking for the answers $x = 5$ and $y = 2$.
- Ask for a few more points like this before putting a point on the x-axis at say (3, 0) and asking: 'What lines is this point on?
- You may have to coax the class to respond $y = 0$ and $x = 3$.

Key Words

- gradient
- intercept
- horizontal run
- vertical rise

Homework

1 State the equation of each straight line shown below.

a 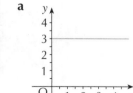 **b** 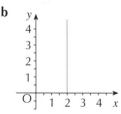 **b** 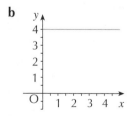 **b**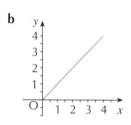

2 Draw sketch graphs of each of the following.

  a $y = 5$ **b** $x = 4$ **c** $y = 2x$

Answers
  1 a $y = 3$ **b** $x = 2$ **c** $y = 4$ **d** $y = x$

Framework objectives – Real-life graphs

Plot graphs arising from real-life problems. Discuss and interpret graphs arising from real situations.

Oral and mental starter

- Tell the class they are going to solve a problem that is best worked on individually.
- A specialist pet-shop owner deals only in cats and budgies.
- The owner has 72 animals altogether (cats and budgies).
- These animals have a total of 200 legs between them.
- How many cats and how many budgies are there at the pet shop?
- Encourage the class to write down the two equations, $4c + 2b = 200$, which gives $2c + b = 100$, and also $c + b = 72$ ($b = 72 - c$).
- Let the students start this problem each on their own. Then after a short while, let them work together in pairs to discuss what they have done and progress further.
- Logical trial and improvement or solving the equations will both lead them to the solution, which is 28 cats and 44 budgies.

Main lesson activity

- Sketch a grid on the board with the pair of axes labelled Temperature (horizontal) from 0 to 30 °C and Deckchairs (vertical) from 0 to 100.
- Give the class the scene. 'At Whitby [or your local seaside resort], will a deckchair attendant hire out more deckchairs when it is hot or cold?' The response should be 'Hot'.
- Draw a cross on the grid at (30, 100), and ask if this is about right. Be prepared to alter it in response to a suitable suggestion.
- Now draw a cross at (5, 0) and ask if this is sensible. Again, alter this in response to a sensible suggestion.
- Draw in a straight line between the two and ask if this shows the likely link between the temperature and the number of deckchairs.
- This could prompt a discussion about how it would not be exactly like that, but it probably shows the correct trend.
- Explain that sketch graphs like this can be used to illustrate trends. They are not necessarily exactly correct, but close to reality.
- Ask if anyone could sketch a graph to illustrate how a hot cup of coffee might cool over half an hour.
- A few volunteers should be ready to show this with axes labelled Time and Temperature, and a graph showing coffee starting with a high temperature, which deceases over time. A straight line is fine for this purpose, but more accurately it would be a curve. Do not discuss this with the class unless they ask at this time.
- Ask the volunteers how they decided which axis to use for time and which for temperature. They may simply be used to putting time on the horizontal axis. Tell the class that when time is involved, it nearly always goes along the horizontal axis.
- **The class can now do Exercise 13E from Pupil Book 1.**

Plenary

- Ask if any of the students would like to illustrate, with a graph on the board, their journey to school. Give them the scales of time and distance from school.
- Discuss the following: where to put starting and ending points; how to show time spent waiting; how to show different speeds.

Key Word
- axes
- trend

1

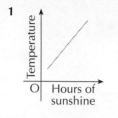 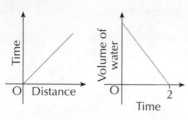 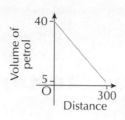

2 a i £1   **ii** £1   **iii** £2   **iv** £2   **v** £5   **vi** £5
  b i Up to 1 hour   **ii** Up to 3 hours   **iii** Up to 6 hours
  c It looks like a series of steps

3

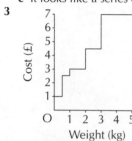

Extension Answers

a i £2   **ii** £2   **iii** £8   **iv** £14   **v** £15   **vi** £19
b

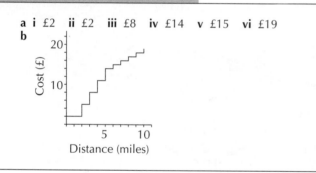

1 An express parcel delivery agency charges £5 for any delivery up to a mile, then another £4 for each mile after that up to 4 miles. For journeys over 4 miles they charge an extra £1 per mile over the 4.

  a How much is charged for the following journeys:

    i half a mile   **ii** 1 mile   **iii** 2 miles   **iv** 4 miles   **v** 7 miles   **vi** 12 miles?

  Draw a step graph to show the charges for journeys up to 12 miles.

2 Look at each of the following graphs and write a short story to go with each graph.

Answers
  1 a i £5   **ii** £5   **iii** £9   **iv** £17   **v** £20   **vi** £25

LESSON 13.6

Framework objectives – Change of subject
Simplify or transform linear expressions.

Oral and mental starter

- Draw on the board the circles shown.
- Tell the class that the numbers in each circle follow the same rule. Can they work out the missing number in the third circle?
- A hint can be: 'Add up pairs – do you notice anything?'
- Eventually, someone will give the correct answer, either as a guess or because he/she has worked it out. Invite the student to tell you (quietly) whether he/she knows how to work it out. Then put the correct answer into the space. (6)
- Ask the student who found the correct answer to give another circle with a number missing at the top, for the rest of the class to try to solve.
- If all or some of the class are struggling, go through the totals of the pairs of numbers in the top and left-hand section. Then ask if they notice any connection between each total and the other number. Hopefully, they will recognise that the total of each pair is exactly three times the other number. Ask the class what the total of the left-hand and top numbers must be to give the number on the right.
- The problem can be extended to involve divisions for those who find the rule quickly.

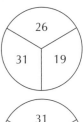

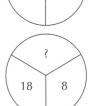

Main lesson activity

- Write on the board $T = 4w + 3$.
- Ask the class what this is. Their response should be 'an equation'.
- Tell them that the equation is written with T as the subject. Ask why this might be. The required response is 'Because that's what it equals.'
- Also tell the class that there are two ways of expressing this relationship between T and w: one in which T is the subject, the other in which w is made the subject.
- Introduce the class to the idea of changing the subject when solving some problems.
- Go through the mapping process, starting with w and finding T:

$$w \longrightarrow \boxed{\times 4} \longrightarrow \boxed{+\,3} \longrightarrow T$$

- Then go through the inverse process:

$$w \longleftarrow \boxed{\div 4} \longleftarrow \boxed{-\,3} \longleftarrow T$$

- Now starting with the T and working through the mapping gives

$$w = \frac{T - 3}{4}$$

- Next, go through another example: $E = 5t + 3$, making t the subject:

$$t \longrightarrow \boxed{\times 5} \longrightarrow \boxed{+\,3} \longrightarrow E$$
$$t \longleftarrow \boxed{\div 5} \longleftarrow \boxed{-\,3} \longleftarrow E$$

This gives $t = \dfrac{E - 3}{5}$.

- Be prepared to give another example: $N = 2m - p$, making m the subject:

$$m \longrightarrow \boxed{\times 2} \longrightarrow \boxed{-\,p} \longrightarrow N$$
$$m \longleftarrow \boxed{\div 2} \longleftarrow \boxed{+\,p} \longleftarrow N$$

This gives $m = \dfrac{N + p}{2}$.

- **The class can now do Exercise 13F from Pupil Book 1.**

138   © Harper*Collins*Publishers Ltd 2003

1 **a** $w = A - k$　**b** $h = \dfrac{A}{b}$　**c** $r = \dfrac{C-D}{3}$　**d** $a = \dfrac{P-2b}{2}$　　**4** **a** $S = 19$　**b** $t = \dfrac{S-a}{3}$　**c** $t = 6$

2 **a** $D = \dfrac{C}{p}$　**b** $t = \dfrac{V-20}{5}$　**c** $h = \dfrac{S-2k}{3}$　**d** $k = 4p - V$　　**5** **a** 7　**b** $t = \dfrac{y+p}{5}$　**c** 4

　e $t = \dfrac{S-4}{5}$　　　　　　　　　　　　　　　　　　**6** **a** 120　**b** $r = \dfrac{V}{12h}$　**c** 1.5

3 **a** $E = 83$　**b** $n = \dfrac{E-8}{5}$　**c** $n = 3$　　　　　**7** 3

Extension Answers

Taking pairs is a quick way. The two end numbers, 1 and 1000, add up to 1001. So too do the next pair of numbers, 2 and 999, all the way to the middle 500 and 501. So you have 500 pairs of numbers adding to 1001, which gives the total of 500 500.

SATs Answers

1 $S = 2P + 1$
2 n^2, $2n$, 6

Plenary

- Ask the class whether they see any similarities between changing subject and solving an equation.
- They may notice shortcuts they can use, but try to avoid teaching them shortcuts before they have had the opportunity to see how to manipulate equations to change the subject.

Homework

1 Rewrite each of the following formulae as indicated:

　a $A = DK$

　　Make K the subject of the formula.

　b $T = 3m + n$

　　Make m the subject of the formula.

　c $F = 2T - k$

　　Make T the subject of the formula.

　d $Q = 4g - 7$

　　Make g the subject of the formula.

2 $d = 8p - 3$

　a Find d when $p = 11$.

　b Make p the subject of the formula.

　c Find p when $d = 53$.

3 $T = m + 3k$

　a Find T when $m = 6$ and $k = 5$.

　b Make k the subject of the formula.

　c Find k when $T = 23$ and $m = 5$.

4 $y = 6x - t$

　a Find y when $x = 3$ and $t = 8$.

　b Make x the subject of the formula.

　c Find x when $y = 21$ and $t = 3$.

Answers

1 **a** $K = \dfrac{A}{D}$　**b** $m = \dfrac{T-n}{3}$　**c** $T = \dfrac{F+k}{2}$

　d $g = \dfrac{Q+7}{4}$

2 **a** $d = 85$　**b** $p = \dfrac{d+3}{8}$　**c** $p = 7$

3 **a** $T = 21$　**b** $k = \dfrac{T-m}{3}$　**c** $k = 6$

4 **a** $y = 10$　**b** $x = \dfrac{y+t}{6}$　**c** $x = 4$

Solving Problems

Framework objectives – Number and measures
Solve more demanding problems and investigate in a range of contexts: number and measures

Oral and mental starter

- Put the numbers 3 and 5 on the board. Ask the class to tell you ways of making as many different numbers as they can using $+$, $-$, $\times$ or by writing the numbers side by side. For example: $3 + 5 = 8$, 53, $5 \times 3 = 15$.
- Repeat with different numbers and then go on to a three-number problem, say 2, 4 and 7. For example: $2 \times 4 + 7 = 15$, $7 \times 2 - 4 = 10$. (Ensure at this stage that the order of operations is the same as in the question.)
- Ask the class to tell you the smallest and largest answers that they can give you.
- Now give the class three numbers and an answer value: for example, 1, 2 and 3 and an answer 7. They have to explain to you how to obtain the answer 7 using only the four rules and the separate digits. For example, $2 + 3 + 1 = 7$.
- Repeat this for different sets of numbers. Change the rules by allowing the class to combine digits to make a two-digit number. For example, use 1 and 2 to make 12.

Main lesson activity

- Explain that the objective of this section is to see whether the class can solve a variety of problems involving measures and the properties of numbers.
- Tell the class that there is often no right or wrong method for solving a problem. With each problem they should ask themselves:
    'Can I spot a pattern?'
    'Can I see a short cut to save working out many unnecessary calculations?'
    'Can I figure out a method for myself?'
- Do they know approximate conversions between imperial and metric units? They should know that $8 \text{ km} \approx 5$ miles, 1 litre ≈ 1.75 pints, $1 \text{ kg} \approx 2.2 \text{ lb}$, and 1 foot $\approx 30 \text{ cm}$. You may want them to write these conversions into their books for reference.
- Ask the class to explain the meaning of the word **consecutive**. Ask them to spell it. Then ask them to give examples of consecutive numbers, consecutive odd numbers and consecutive even numbers.
- Now ask the class to give you two consecutive numbers that add up to, say, 21.
- Repeat using different numbers or using just odd and even numbers.
- This activity can be extended using other types of number, such as primes or factors. For example, ask for two factors of 10 which add up to 7.

- **The class can now do Exercise 14A from Pupil Book 1.**

1 6 and 7

2 a

Powers of 3	Working out	Answer	Units digit
3^1	3	3	3
3^2	3×3	9	9
3^3	$3 \times 3 \times 3$	27	7
3^4	$3 \times 3 \times 3 \times 3$	81	1
3^5	$3 \times 3 \times 3 \times 3 \times 3$	243	3
3^6	$3 \times 3 \times 3 \times 3 \times 3 \times 3$	729	9
3^7	$3 \times 3 \times 3 \times 3 \times 3 \times 3 \times 3$	2187	7
3^8	$3 \times 3 \times 3 \times 3 \times 3 \times 3 \times 3 \times 3$	6561	1

b 1

3 12 seconds

4 a 11 and 13   **b** $4 \times 31 = 124$

5

4	3	8
9	5	1
2	7	6

2	9	4
7	5	3
6	1	8

6	2	7
6	5	4
3	8	4

6 15 years old

7 $5 \times 3 = 15$ km

8 7 lb, as 3 kg is approximately 6.6 lb.

9 10 miles, as 10 miles is approximately 16 km.

10 1 square mile, as 1 mile (1.6 km) is greater than 1 km.

Plenary

- Refer the class to the powers of 3 problem (Exercise 14A, Question 2).
- Ask them what happened with the units digits.
- Now write table headings on the board, as shown below.
- Ask different students to fill in the columns.
- Encourage them to state what will happen if the table is continued.

Powers of 2	Answer	Units digit
2^1	2	2
2^2	4	4
2^3	8	8
2^4	16	6
2^5	32	2

- Finish off by pointing out that there are lots of patterns in mathematics and that patterns are often used to solve problems.

Key Words

- solve
- problems
- investigate
- consecutive
- digit
- product
- number
- measure

Homework

1 Two consecutive numbers add up to 25. What are the numbers?

2 Two consecutive odd numbers add up to 20. What are the numbers?

3 Two consecutive even numbers add up to 38. What are the numbers?

4 A map has a scale of 1 cm to 4 km. The distance between two places on the map is 2.5 cm. What is the actual distance between the two places?

5 Which is the greater length, 3 feet or 1 metre? Use the fact that 1 foot ≈ 30 centimetres.

6 Which is the greater, 9 pints or 5 litres? Use the fact that 1 litre ≈ 1.75 pints.

7 Which is the greater mass, 4 kg or 9 pounds? Use the fact that 1 kg ≈ 2.2 pounds.

Answers

1 12 and 13
2 9 and 11
3 18 and 20
4 10 km
5 1 metre, as 3 feet = 90 cm
6 9 pints, as 5 litres = 8.75 pints
7 9 pounds, as 4 kg = 8.8 lb

LESSON 14.2

Framework objectives – Using words and diagrams to solve problems

Represent problems mathematically, making correct use of symbols, words, diagrams, tables and graphs. *(Year 7 objective.)*

Break a complex calculation into simpler steps, choosing and using appropriate and efficient operations, methods and resources, including ICT. *(Year 7 objective.)*

Oral and mental starter

- Write £5 on the board. Tell the class that a person is paid £5 an hour. Ask them questions about this. For example:
  'How much would the person be paid for 7 hours work?'
  'How many hours would the person need to work to be paid £45?'
- Ask the class to explain how they worked out each answer. Now ask them to give you some facts. For example: for 10 hours work the person will be paid £50. Get some students to check whether the fact is correct.
- Now draw a flow chart for two rules, say add 5 and double the result. Give them an input number and ask for the output. When they give the answer write down the expression: (Number + 5) × 2.
- Keep changing each rule and writing down the expression.
- Finally, ask the class to give you a rule and the corresponding expression.

Main lesson activity

- Tell the class that the aim of this lesson is to solve problems using algebra, using tables or diagrams.
- Leading on from the starter, ask the students to each think of a number and then double it. Write down on the board:
  $2x =$ or $2 \times$ the number =
- Then ask a student for his/her answer. Write it in the space. For example:
  $2x = 18$ or $2 \times$ the number = 18
- Ask the other students to give you his/her original number. Ask them how they found it.
- Now say to the class that this could be turned into a window-cleaning problem. A window cleaner charges £2 per window. If the total bill is £18, how many windows does he clean?
- Show the class the equation: $2x = 18$.
- Ask them how the equation changes when the rate per window changes.
- Develop this by including a second stage. For example, ask the class to each think of a number, double it and then add 3. Write on the board:
  $2x + 3 =$ or $2 \times$ the number + 3 =
- Now show them the flow chart method, telling the class that the final answer is 17.

- Point out that want them to work backwards. Ask a student to explain the reverse steps and then draw on the board the reverse flow chart.

- **The class can now do Exercise 14B from Pupil Book 1.**

1 72 kg

2 24

3 a 8 × number of days   **b** £80
   c i £30   **ii** £40   **iii** £60

4 9

5 10

6 12

7 a £550   **b** £3250

8 a   **b** 15
   c Add pattern
     number to
     previous total

9 99. The label is one less than the
   number of the square.

10 31, because 31 teams are knocked out

Extension Answers

4 and 9; formula is n^2; pattern is square numbers

Plenary

Key Words

- Invite two students to stand up. Tell the class that these two students are in a competition. The winner is the first one to answer a question.
- Ask a mental arithmetic question: for example, $1 \times 2 \times 3 \times 4$.
- The student who gives the correct answer remains standing.
- Write on the board a table with two headings

Number of players	Number knocked out

- Now start with four students. Play a knockout game (two semifinals and a final).
- Repeat with 8 pupils.
- Complete the table.

Number of players	Number knocked out
2	1
4	3
8	7

- Ask the class to spot the pattern.

Key Words:
- algebra
- table
- sum
- difference
- formula
- flow chart
- example

Homework

1 Two numbers add up to 37. One of the numbers is 15. What is the other number?

2 The sum of two numbers is 21 and the difference is 7. What are the numbers?

3 Two parcels weigh 11 kg altogether. The heavier parcel weighs 3 kg more than the lighter parcel. How much does each parcel weigh?

4 Two pieces of wood are made from a plank 4 metres long. One piece is 1 metre shorter than the other piece. How long is each piece?

5 I think of a number, double it and add 4. The answer is 22.

Copy and complete the flow chart. Then work out the number.

6 I think of a number, multiply it by 4 and subtract 6. The answer is 30.

Copy and complete the flow chart. Then work out the number.

7 I think of a number divide it by 2 it and add 7. The answer is 25

Copy and complete the flow chart. Then work out the number.

Answers

1 22

2 7 and 14

3 7 kg and 4 kg

4 2.5 m and 1.5 m

5 9

6 9

7 36

LESSON 14.3

Framework objectives – Logical solutions and best value

Use logical argument to establish the truth of a statement; give solutions to an appropriate degree of accuracy in the context of the problem.

Understand the significance of a counter-example. *(Year 7 objective.)*

Oral and mental starter

- The students can use show me boards, number fans or a sheet of paper to show their answers.
- Ask them to show you: a multiple of 3, a multiple of 4, a multiple of 3 and 4, and a multiple of 3 and 4, the digits of which add up to 6.
- Repeat this for several different values.
- Now ask them, in pairs, to show you: two consecutive numbers, two consecutive numbers with a sum of 21, two consecutive numbers with a product of 20, two consecutive odd numbers with a sum of 16, two consecutive odd numbers with a product of 35.
- Give the class a fairly large number, say 72, and ask them to give you ways of forming it from two other numbers. Try to get examples with each operator.

Main lesson activity

- This lesson aims to reinforce student knowledge of terms such as **multiple**, **factor** and **consecutive**, as well as to look at logical solutions to problems, at the use of examples to show whether something is true or false and at best-value problems.
- Explain to the class that many problems can be solved by different methods, including trial and improvement.
- Show that, for example, in a subtraction either a conventional method could be used or they could build up to their answer on a number line. Take, for example, $43 - 11$:

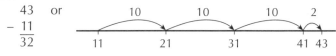

$$\begin{array}{r} 43 \\ - 11 \\ \hline 32 \end{array}$$

Answer = 32

- Show the class that in the case of division, the problem can be turned round to build up by repeated addition or multiplication. Take, for example, $180 \div 3 = 60$:
  $3 \times 10 = 30, 3 \times 20 = 60, 3 \times 40 = 120, 3 \times 60 = 60 + 120 = 180$
  so, $3 \times 60 = 180$ gives $180 \div 3 = 60$
- Explain that when solving a missing number problem, as at the start of the exercise, either they could figure it out part-by-part or they could use a calculator to experiment. Warn them that using a calculator could be a lengthy process.
- Ask the class to add together in their heads any two even numbers they choose. Ask them to put up their hands if their answer is even. Tell them that they will need to know facts like Even + Even → Even. They could make a list in their books of the four combinations for addition and the four combinations for multiplication, as shown:
  Even + Even → Even
  Even + Odd → Odd
  Odd + Even → Odd
  Odd + Odd → Even
  Even × Even → Even
  Even × Odd → Even
  Odd × Even → Even
  Odd × Odd → Odd
- Finally, ask the students how they would work out a best-value problem. For example: three items for £9 or four items for £10.
- Write out on the board a valid method for them to use as an example.

- **The class can now do Exercise 14C from Pupil Book 1.**

Exercise 14C Answers

1 **a** $32 + 17 = 49$ **b** $43 + 33 = 76$ **c** $132 + 17 = 149$ **d** $87 - 42 = 45$
   e $238 - 121 = 117$ **f** $135 \times 4 = 540$
2 For example: $1 + 3 = 4$
3 For example: $2 + 4 = 6$
4 For example: $1 + 2 = 3$
5 For example: $3 \times 5 = 15$
6 For example: $3 \times 4 = 12$
7 2 litres at £2.40
8 **a** 6 litres for £12 **b** 8 kg for £18 **c** 300 g for £5 **d** 4 chocolate bars for 90p
9 750 g

Plenary

- Look at a best-value problem. Take, for example, three bottles of water: 35p for 500 ml, £1.20 for 2 litres and £1.95 for 5 litres.
- Remind the class that there are 100 ml in 1 litre. Ask them to look at the small bottle and tell you how much it will be for 1 litre, 2 litres, 5 litres.
- Encourage them to say that the small bottler is the most expensive.
- Repeat with the 2 litre bottle.
- Point out that, in this case, the largest is the cheapest but that is not always so. Use another example to show this.

Key Words

- [ ] **proof**
- [ ] **counter-example**
- [ ] **justify**
- [ ] **conclude**
- [ ] **solution**
- [ ] **solve**

Homework

1 Copy and complete the following number problems, filling in the missing digits:

   a $\begin{array}{r} 2\square \\ + \ \square\,3 \\ \hline 7\ 6 \end{array}$ **b** $\begin{array}{r} 9\square \\ + \ \square\,4 \\ \hline 1\ 1\ 9 \end{array}$ **c** $\begin{array}{r} \square\,9 \\ - \ 1\square \\ \hline 2\ 8 \end{array}$ **d** $\begin{array}{r} \square\,7 \\ \times \quad 2 \\ \hline 3\ 4 \end{array}$

2 Write down an example to show that when you double a whole number, you get an even number.

3 Write down two examples to show that when you halve an even number, you may get an even number or you may get an odd number.

4 Which is the better value for money?

   a Six pies for £3 or ten pies for £6

   b Twelve pencils for £1.44 or ten pencils for £1.10

5 A recipe for four people uses 200 g of flour. How much flour would the recipe need for

   a eight people?   **b** six people?

Answers
   1 **a** $23 + 53 = 76$ **b** $95 + 24 = 119$ **c** $39 - 11 = 28$ **d** $17 \times 2 = 34$
   2 For example: $2 \times 3 = 6$
   3 For example: $4 \div 2 = 2$, $6 \div 2 = 3$
   4 **a** Six pies for £3 **b** ten pencils for £1.10
   5 **a** 400 g **b** 300 g

LESSON 14.4

Oral and mental starter

- Take a counting stick.

- Tell the class that *one* section is equal to 5 km. Ask them what distance three sections are equal to. Repeat for different numbers of sections and different units.
- Now tell the class, for example, that five sections are worth £15. Ask them what six sections are worth. Repeat this for many different values, but use appropriate numbers so that any divisions can be done mentally.
- This activity could be developed by using fractions. For example, tell the class that $\frac{3}{5}$ of the stick weighs 40 kg, and then ask what the stick weighs.

Main lesson activity

- The aim is to use proportions to solve practical, everyday problems. In addition, the class needs to recall some of the conversions given in Lesson 14.1.
- Ask them which conversions they can remember. Write these on the board (8 km ≈ 5 miles, 1 litre ≈ 1.75 pints, 1 kg ≈ 2.2 pounds, 1 foot ≈ 30 cm).
- Ask them to look at, say, 8 km ≈ 5 miles and give you a related fact. For example, 16 km ≈ 10 miles. Now ask the class how they would work out the number of miles in 20 km. Encourage them to offer different methods.
- Now write two distances on the board: for example, 8 km and 16 km. Tell them that these represent a journey of 16 km, with a stop at 8 km. Ask them what fraction (or proportion) of the journey is covered after the 8 km stop.
- Repeat the question for different numbers. For example, change 8 km to 4 km.
- Now change the question by saying, for example, that you have £5 in one pocket and £15 in another pocket, and asking what fraction (or proportion) of the money is in the first pocket.

- **The class can now do Exercise 14D from Pupil Book 1.**

1 $1\frac{1}{5}$ or 0.2 or 20%
2 $\frac{3}{4}$
3 $\frac{1}{4}$
4 **a** 6 litres blue and 14 litres yellow **b** 1.5 litres blue and 3.5 litres yellow
5 **a** 15 miles **b** 40 km
6 **a** 4 feet **b** 0.5 feet **c** 1.5 feet
7 £30
8 £9
9 £18
10 **a** 180 miles **b** 15 miles **c** 195 miles
11 **a** 24 km **b** 36 km **c** 48 km
12 **a** 80 litres **b** 20 litres **c** 60 litres
13 £2

Plenary

● Explain that, for example, travelling at 60 miles per hour means travelling 60 miles in *one* hour. In other words, it means travelling one mile in one minute.
● Ask the class how far you would travel in, for example, 2 hours, 3 hours, 4 hours, 30 minutes, at 60 miles per hour.
● Repeat for different speeds.
● Tell the class that you travelled 100 miles in 4 hours and ask them how far you travelled in one hour. In response to their answer, say this means you were travelling at 25 miles per hour.

- **proportion**
- **fraction**
- **decimal**
- **percentage**
- **ratio**
- **litres**
- **volume**
- **kilogram**

Homework

1 A family spends £30 at the cinema on tickets and £5 on refreshments. What proportion of the spending is on refreshments?

2 A bus travels at 12 miles per hour:

   a How far will it travel in 15 minutes? **b** How far will it travel in 20 minutes?

   c How far will it travel in 35 minutes? **d** How far will it travel in 1 hour 20 minutes?

3 Five burgers cost £3.50. What will 15 burgers cost?

4 Three plants cost £18. What will six plants cost?

5 10 pens cost £12. What will one pen cost?

6 1 kg is approximately equal to 2.2 pounds:

   a How many pounds are equal to 4 kg? **b** How many kilograms are equal to 11 pounds?

Answers

1 $\frac{1}{7}$
2 **a** 3 miles **b** 4 miles **c** 7 miles **d** 16 miles
3 £10.50
4 £36
5 £1.20
6 **a** 8.8 pounds **b** 5 kg

LESSON 14.5

Framework objectives – Ratio

Solve simple problems about ratio and proportion using informal strategies.

Oral and mental starter

- Use two target boards:

1:2	1:3	3:2	4:1	5:2
$\frac{1}{2}$	$\frac{1}{3}$	$\frac{1}{4}$	$\frac{2}{3}$	$\frac{3}{4}$

3	5	2	4	1	6	8
10	7	9	12	15	18	20

- Ask the students to identify pairs of numbers from the right-hand target board and match them up to ratios or fractions in left-hand board. For example, 3 and 6 are in the ratio 1 : 2 or 3 is $\frac{1}{2}$ of 6.
- Now cover the left-hand board and ask students to give equivalent ratios or fractions using their own numbers.
- This activity can be developed by adding decimals or percentages to the left-hand target board.
- Students could make lists of equivalent ratios or fractions in their exercise books.

Main lesson activity

- Tell the class that the aim of this lesson is to learn how to solve simple problems about ratio.
- Ask them to simplify, for example, 6 : 4. Then ask them to simplify a ratio with both units the same: for example, 6 m : 4 m. Point out that when the units are the same, the units can be cancelled out to give the same answer as before. Write an example of each type on the board for them to copy into their books.
- Repeat for different ratios.
- Point out that when the units are different they must be changed to the same unit. Give the class a simple example, say, 60 minutes : 2 hours.
- Ask them to explain what they understand by the ratio 1 : 2. Refer back to the starter with fractions, if necessary. Select two girls and one boy, asking them to stand up. State that you have 30 sweets to share out. Ask how many the girls will get. Now ask the class to explain how they worked out their answer. At this stage, ensure that one part of the ratio is always 1 : for example, 3 : 1 or 1 : 4.
- Change the numbers and the number of girls and boys used and repeat.
- Write out an example for them to show them how you want them to present their solutions on paper.
- Now reverse the problem. Again using, for example, two girls and one boy, tell the class that you have already given equal numbers of coloured pencils to the three students. Tell them that the girls have 24 pencils altogether. Now ask the class how many the boy has.
- Change the numbers and the number of girls and boys used and repeat.

- **The class can now do Exercise 14E from Pupil Book 1.**

1 **a** 3:2 **b** 2:5 **c** 3:1 **d** 2:3 **e** 1:4 **f** 4:1 **g** 4:1 **h** 4:3 **i** 1:3
  j 4:1 **k** 5:1 **l** 4:1 **m** 2:5 **n** 5:1 **o** 10:7 **p** 2:15 **q** 4:1 **r** 4:1
  s 1:15 **t** 1:5
2 **a** 3:2 **b** 2:5 **c** 3:1 **d** 2:3 **e** 1:4 **f** 4:1
3 **a** 2:1 **b** 1:4 **c** 1:1 **d** 5:1 **e** 2:1 **f** 1:2
4 44 items.
5 160 females
6 60 children
7 16 carp
8 300 brown loaves
9 20 litres

Extension Answers

Volume ratio is the cube of the side ratio. Surface area ratio is the square of the length ratio. The length ratio is the same.

Sats Answers

1 **b** 12 **c** → ☐÷ 2 ☐ → **d** 9
2 **a** 3 **b** ½ **c** 15
3 **a** 6 litres of red and 14 litres of blue **b** 6.5 litres of yellow and 3.5 litres of red
4 **a** 1:3 **b** 1:1.5 or 2:3 **c** One carton of orange juice
5 **a** £345 **b** 36 words

Plenary

Key Words

- Write 60 on the board. Ask the class to split it into two numbers so that one is twice the other. Write down 40:20.
- Change the starting number to, for example, 12 and repeat. Write down 8:4.
- Repeat for different numbers. Ask the class to look at all the ratios and comment on them. Hopefully, they will realise that all the ratios are equivalent to 2:1.
- Finally, tell them that you have already divided a quantity in the ratio 2:1 and that the smaller part was 7000. Ask them what the larger part was and also the total.

☐ **ratio**
☐ **unitary method**
☐ **divide**
☐ **problem**
☐ **percentage**
☐ **ratio notation**

Homework

1 Simplify each of these ratios.

  a 8:4   **b** 5:15   **c** 14:7   **d** 12:9   **e** 15:5   **f** 18:12   **g** 3:12

  h 24:18   **i** 4:16

2 **a** £10:£8   **b** 33 m:3 m   **c** £1:£5   **d** 10 kg:4 kg   **e** 5000 mm:1000 mm

  f 2 hours:8 hours

3 **a** 1 hour:20 minutes   **b** 2 weeks:2 days   **c** 2 metres:80 cm

4 In a test Charlotte scores twice as many as Eleanor. Altogether they score 36 marks. How many marks does each girl score?

Answers
  1 **a** 2:1 **b** 1:3 **c** 2:1 **d** 4:3 **e** 3:1 **f** 3:2 **g** 1:4 **h** 4:3 **i** 1:4
  2 **a** 5:4 **b** 11:1 **c** 1:5 **d** 5:2 **e** 5:1 **f** 1:4
  3 **a** 3:1 **b** 7:1 **c** 5:2
  4 Charlotte scores 24 and Eleanor scores 12

Shape, Space and Measures 4

Framework objectives – Plans and elevations

Use 2-D representations to visualise 3-D shapes and deduce some of their properties.

Know and use geometric properties of cuboids and shapes made from cuboids; begin to use plans and elevations.

Oral and mental starter

- *Imagine* a large cube. How many faces does it have? How many edges does it have?
- Check that the students know the correct answers – six faces and 12 edges.
- Now *imagine* a cube on which the top and front faces are coloured red and the other faces are coloured blue.
- How many edges are there where a red face touches another red face?
- How many edges are there where a blue face touches another blue face?
- How many edges are there where a red face touches a blue face?
- The class can be shown a model of the cube to explain the answers: 1, 5 and 6.

Main lesson activity

- The work in this section involves a good deal of complex drawing on isometric paper, which students often find difficult. It is therefore suggested that the work should cover two lessons.
- At the start of the lesson the class should be given sheets of centimetre isometric dotted paper and centimetre-squared paper.
- The class should be encouraged to work in pairs or small groups, as students can often help each other.
- Multi-link cubes should also be made available for students to construct the shapes shown on the isometric grids.

Lesson 15.1
- Explain to the class that the lesson is about how to draw 3-D shapes on isometric paper and how to draw different views of the shapes on squared paper.
- Draw, on the board or on a prepared OHT, the 3-D shape shown on the right. The shape could also be made out of multi-link cubes.
- Ask the class to copy it on isometric paper, and show them the correct way to use isometric paper.
- Explain that the dots must always be in vertical columns.
- Explain that a 3-D shape can be viewed from different angles:
    a **plan** is the view of a 3-D shape when it is looked at from above (a bird's eye view).
    an **elevation** is the view of a 3-D shape when it is looked at from the front or from the side.
- The class can now draw the plan and the two elevations, as shown below, on squared paper:

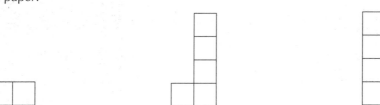

Plan from A   Front elevation from B   Side elevation from C

© HarperCollins*Publishers* Ltd 2003

- The class can now start Exercise 15A from Pupil Book 1.

   Lesson 15.2

- The class can continue with Exercise 15A from Pupil Book 1.
- Multi-link cubes and a collection of different 3-D shapes should also be made available for this lesson.

Exercise 15A Answers

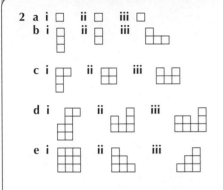
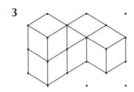

4 a cube (or cuboid)
   b cuboid (or cylinder)
   c square-based pyramid
   d tetrahedron
   e cylinder (or sphere)
   f triangular prism

Extension Answers

   1 a E, F, H, I, L   b the letter must consist of only horizontal and vertical lines

Plenary

Key Words

☐ **elevation**
☐ **isometric**
☐ **plan view**
☐ **view**

- Ask individual students to explain the following terms: plan, front elevation and side elevation.
- Display some shapes made from multi-link cubes for students to draw plans and elevations of at the board.
- Discuss with the class what would happen if they were to view any of these shapes from below (a worm's eye view) or from the back.

Homework

1 Draw an accurate copy of this cuboid on an isometric grid.

   6 cm

   2 cm

   4 cm

2 For each of the following 3-D shapes below, draw on centimetre-squared paper:

   i the plan   **ii**   the front elevation   **iii** the side elevation.

   a   b   c

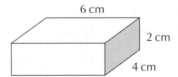
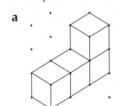
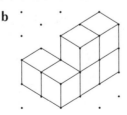
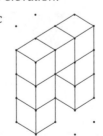

   Answers
   2 a i   ii   iii   b i   ii   iii   c i   ii   iii

Framework objectives – Scale drawings
Make simple scale drawings.

Oral and mental starter

- A starter to practice estimating length.
- Students will need rulers and possibly a tape measure for this activity. It is best done using individual white boards, but students can give their answers orally.
- Ask a student to select an object in the classroom.
- Ask the rest of the class to estimate the length of the object and to write their answer on their white boards.
- Ask the first student to measure the actual length of the object.
- The students can now show their estimates on their white boards. Some discussion of the units used may be a useful exercise.
- The student whose estimate is closest to the actual length wins a point.
- The activity can be repeated with a different student selecting another object.

Main lesson activity

- Explain to the class that the lesson is about using and making scale drawings.
- Draw on the board or OHT a scale drawing to show the dimensions of a room in school, for example a classroom, the school hall or the gym.
- You could provide a tape measure or metre rule and ask a student to measure the classroom for you.

8 m

6 m

scale: 1 cm to 2 m

- Explain to the class the importance of choosing a sensible scale. It might be worth pointing out that if you double the scale, the scale drawing is halved in size.
- Show the class how to find the actual length and width of the room by using the scale.

- **The class can now do Exercise 15B from Pupil Book 1.**
- If time is available towards the end of term, the class can work in groups to complete extra practical work for a display in the classroom. For example, students can draw plans for the school playground, the sports field or the staff car park.

Exercise 15B Answers

1 **a** 20 m **b** 50 m **c** 35 m **d** 78 m **e** 63 m
2 **a** 25 m **b** 15 m **c** ≈ 29 m
3 **a** 1 cm to 2 m **b** 6 m **c** 48 m²
4 **a** 16 cm **b** 6 cm **c** 2 cm **d** 3 m **e** 2.5 m **f** 1.2 m
5 **a i** 6 m by 4 m **ii** 4 m by 2 m **iii** 6 m by 4 m **iv** 5 m by 4 m **b** 68 m²

Plenary

● Show the class a map of Britain.
● Ask the class to guess the scale for the map.
● Tell the class the answer.
● Have some other maps with different scales to repeat this with.

Homework

1 The lines below are drawn using a scale 1 cm to 4 m. Write down the length each line represents.

  a ─────────────

  b ─────────────────────────

  c ───────────────

  d ──────────────────────

  e ────────────────────────────

2 The diagram shown is a scale drawing of Mr Peters' garden:

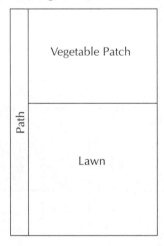

Vegetable Patch

Path

Lawn

Scale: 1 cm to 2 m

  a Find the actual dimensions of the garden.

  b Find the actual dimensions of the lawn.

  c Find the actual dimensions of the vegetable patch.

  d Find the actual area of the path.

3 The length of a netball court is 30 m and its width is 16 m. On centimetre-squared paper, draw a plan of the netball court, using a scale of 1 cm to 4 m.

Answers
  1 **a** 12 m **b** 28 m **c** 18 m **d** 21.6 m **e** 34.8 m
  2 **a** 12 m by 8 m **b** 7 m by 7 m **c** 7 m by 5 m **d** 12 m²
  3 Scale drawing with sides 7.5 cm by 4 cm

Framework objectives – Coordinates in all four quadrants

Use conventions and notation for 2-D coordinates in all four quadrants; find coordinates of points determined by geometric information.

Oral and mental starter

- This is a revision starter on coordinates, using a practical activity that requires a coordinate grid and two dice of different colours (e.g., red and blue).
- Explain to the class that they are going to play the game 'Four in a line'.
- The game can be played in pairs or as a class activity.
- On prepared sheets or on an OHT, draw a grid with x- and y-axes going from 0 to 6.
- Explain that one person throws the two dice. The score on the red dice gives the x-coordinate and the score on the blue dice gives the y-coordinate of a point. The person then plots that point on the grid.
- Another person then throws the dice and plots her point on the grid.
- The game continues until a person wins by plotting four points in a line. The line can be horizontal, vertical or diagonal.

Main lesson activity

- Explain that **coordinates** are used to locate a point on a grid. Draw, on the board or on an OHT, the grid shown on the right.
- Explain the meaning of axes, the x-axis, the y-axis and the origin.
- A coordinate is written in the form (x, y).
- The first number is the x-coordinate, which is the number of units across the grid.
- The second number is the y-coordinate, which is the number of units up the grid. Use the point A as an example.
- The point A has coordinates (4, 3) and can be written as A(4, 3).
- Plot other points on the grid and ask the class to write down their coordinates.
- Emphasise the need to plot coordinates using a cross.

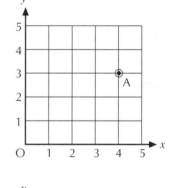

- Explain that the grid can be extended to use negative numbers. Draw, on the board or on an OHT, the grid shown on the right.
- Explain that the grid is divided into four quadrants.
- Ask the class to copy the grid and plot the points A, B, C and D.
- Explain how to write down the coordinates of the four points: A(4, 2), B(–4, 2), C (–4, –2) and D(4, –2).
- Plot other points on the grid and ask the class to write down their coordinates.

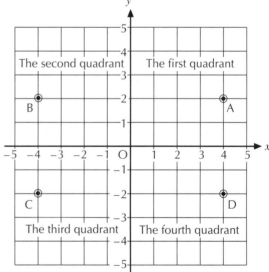

- **The class can now do Exercise 15C from Pupil Book 1.**

Exercise 15C Answers

1 P(5, 4), Q(4, 1), R(2, 2), S(1, 0), T(0, 3)
2 c D(4, 1)
3 A(2, 3), B(5, 1), C(–3, 4), D(–3, 0), E(–4, –2), F(0, –4), G(1, –2), H(4, –5)
4 b W
5 c Z(–3, 4) **d** (0, 1)

Extension Answers

The *y*-coordinate is always 2 more than the *x*-coordinate.

Plenary

- Have a prepared, large grid with axes from –10 to 10 and several points plotted on it.
- Ask the class to write down the coordinates of the points as you point to them.
- Explain that the next stage is to find, using algebra, relationships for coordinates that follow a pattern.

Homework

1 Write down the coordinates of the points P, Q, R and S on the grid.

2 **a** Draw a grid as in Question 1 and plot the points A(1, 4), B(5, 4), C(5, 1) and D(1, 1).

   b Join the points to form the rectangle ABCD.

   c What are the coordinates of the mid-point of AB?

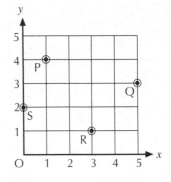

3 Write down the coordinates of the points A, B, C, D, E, F, G and H on the grid.

4 **a** Draw a grid as in Question 3 and plot the points P(1, 4), Q(4, 2) and R(1, –4)

   b The points form three vertices of a kite PQRS. Plot the point S and draw the kite.

   c Write down the coordinates of the point S.

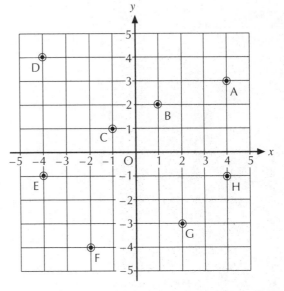

Answers
  1 P(1, 4), Q(5, 3), R(3, 1), S(0, 2)
  2 **c** (3, 4)
  3 A(4, 3), B(1, 2), C(–1, 1), D(–4, 4), E(–4, –1), F(–2, –4), G(2, –3), H(4, –1)
  4 **c** S(–2, 2)

Framework objectives – To construct a triangle given three sides

Use straight edge and compasses to construct a triangle, given three sides (SSS); use ICT to explore this construction.

Oral and mental starter

● This is a starter to help with spelling and knowledge of mathematical terms.
● Write on the board: Richard Of York Gave Battle In Vain.
● Ask the students if they recognise this mnemonic for the colours of the rainbow: Red, Orange, Yellow, Green, Blue, Indigo, Violet (a mnemonic is an aid to help remember facts).
● Ask the students to write down the names of all the special quadrilaterals that they have met (square, rectangle, parallelogram, rhombus, kite, arrowhead, trapezium).
● Ask the class to work in pairs and, in five or ten minutes, invent a suitable mnemonic for the names of the quadrilaterals.

Main lesson activity

● Remind the class about the two constructions they used for triangles in Year 7:
    a triangle given two sides and the included angle (SAS):

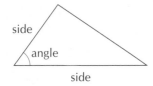

    a triangle given two angles and the included side (ASA):

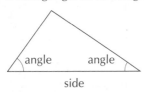

● Explain that the lesson is about how to construct a triangle given three sides (SSS). For this lesson the students will require a ruler and compasses.
● Draw a sketch of such a triangle on the board.
● Ask the students to draw the triangle shown in stages as described below:

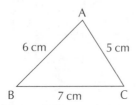

    Draw the line BC 7 cm long
    Set compasses to a radius of 6 cm and, with centre at B, draw a large arc above BC.
    Set compasses to a radius of 5 cm and, with centre at C, draw a large arc to intersect the first arc.
    The intersection of the arcs is A.
    Join AB and AC to complete the triangle.
    The construction lines should be left on the diagram.

● **The class can now do Exercise 15D from Pupil Book 1.**

4 A right-angled triangle.
6 The sum of the two shorter sides is smaller than the longest side.

Plenary

● Draw a sketch of this triangle on the board:

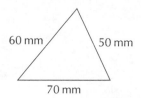

● Ask the class how they would construct the triangle.
● Now draw a sketch of the following triangle on the board:

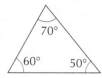

● Ask the class how they would construct this triangle.
● They should say it is not possible, as it could be drawn any size because you do not know the lengths of any of the sides.
● If time allows, it may be possible to discuss the idea of similar shapes.
.

Homework

1 Construct each of the following triangles (remember to label all the lines):

a

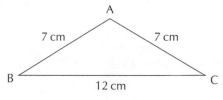

b

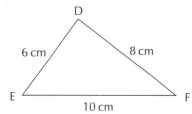

c

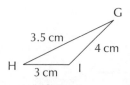

2 Construct the triangle XYZ with XY = 7 cm, XZ = 6 cm and YZ = 5 cm.
3 Construct an equilateral triangle with sides of length 4 cm.

Framework objectives – Loci

Find simple loci, both by reasoning and by using ICT, to produce shapes and paths, e.g. an equilateral triangle.

Use units of measurement to estimate, calculate and solve problems in everyday contexts involving length, area, volume, capacity, mass, time, angle and bearings; know rough metric equivalents of imperial measures in daily use (feet, miles, pounds, pints, gallons).

Oral and mental starter

- Describe to the class the route that Carol takes from her house to her local post office:

    Leave home and turn left at the front gate.
    Walk straight on for 100 m.
    The post office is on the left.

- Ask a student to describe Carol's route back home.
- Now extend her route.

    Leave home and turn left at the front gate.
    Walk straight on for 100 m.
    Turn left at the crossroads.
    Walk straight on for 50 m.
    The post office is on the left.

- Ask another student to describe her route back home.
- Now extend her route again.

    Leave home and turn left at the front gate.
    Walk straight on for 100 m.
    Turn left at the crossroads.
    Walk straight on for 50 m.
    Turn right at the church.
    Walk straight on for 200 m.
    The post office is on the left.

- Ask another student to describe her route back home.
- This activity can be changed to suit the ability of the class.

Main lesson activity

- Explain to the class that **locus** is another name for the path taken by a moving object.
- The students should copy the definition of a locus into their books: 'A locus is a set of points that satisfy a given set of conditions or a rule.'
  It is useful to think of a locus as a path traced out by a single moving point. The plural of locus is loci.
- Explain to the class the following practical examples of loci.
- A conker swung around on a piece of string of length 20 cm. A sketch of the locus of the conker is given:

    The locus can be described as a circle with a radius of 20 cm.

- A man walking across a football pitch so that he is equidistant from both sets of goal posts. Explain that equidistant means 'the same distance'. A sketch of the man's locus is given:
- A cue ball moving across a snooker table into a pocket, with the ball equidistant from two sides of the table. A sketch of the locus of the ball is given:

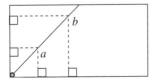

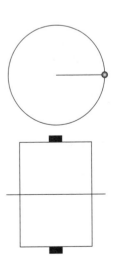

- Choose any two points on the locus (*a* and *b*) and demonstrate that the ball is always equidistant from the table's sides when on this path.

- **The class can now do Exercise 15E from Pupil Book 1.**

1 **a** a curve in the shape of a parabola   **b** a circle   **c** a straight line
   d a semi-circle   **e** a straight line   **f** an arc of a circle
2 The perpendicular bisector of the line joining the two barns.
3 The bisector of the angle between the two fences.
4 **b** a semi-circle
5 **a** a circle with radius 10 cm   **b** a circle with radius 20 cm

Extension Answers

1

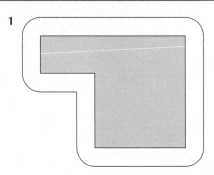

2 The car park is divided by the perpendicular bisector of the line that joins the two meters.

Key Words

☐ **equidistant**
☐ **locus, loci**

Plenary

● Ask the students to make up their own loci and to sketch them at the board, using examples similar to those in Exercise 15E.

Homework

1 Draw a sketch and describe the locus for each of the following situations:

   a the trail left on the ground by a snail

   b the path of the tip of a windscreen wiper on a car

   c the path of a ball thrown upwards into the air

   d the path of a satellite as it travels around the Earth

   e the path of a boy on a helter-skelter at the fun-fair.

2 The diagram shows two towns, A and B:

   A   B
   ○   ○

   A motorway is to be built so that it is equidistant from both towns:

   On a sketch of the diagram, draw the locus of the path that the motorway will take.

3 The diagram shows a ball rolling along the ground:

   a On a sketch of the diagram, draw the locus

   of the centre of the ball as it rolls along the ground.

   b Describe the locus of the centre of the ball.

4 The diagram shows a boat in a harbour:

   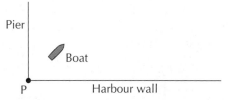

   The boat sets off from point P and steers so that it keeps equidistant from the pier and the harbour wall.

   On a sketch of the diagram, draw the locus of the boat.

   Answers
   1 **a** a curved zig-zagged line   **b** an arc of a circle
      c a straight line   **d** a circle   **e** a spiral shape
   2 The perpendicular bisector of the line joining the towns.
   3 A straight line parallel to the ground.
   4 The bisector of the angle between the pier and the harbour wall.

Framework objectives – Bearings

Use bearings to specify direction.

Oral and mental starter

- This is an activity called '180', to make the students familiar with pairs of numbers that add to 180.
- The target board shown can be drawn on the board or students can be given prepared sheets.
- The aim is to cross off the pairs of numbers that sum to 180 as quickly as possible until one number is left.
- The answer is 72.

104	140	36	112	169
157	89	72	99	125
55	162	47	76	65
81	68	40	11	144
133	115	23	91	18

Main lesson activity

- Start the lesson by reminding the students of various facts about angles:
  1 The angles on a straight line add up to 180°.
  2 The angles in a complete turn add up to 360°.
- Show the class a compass or draw on the board the main compass points.
- Remind the class that the four main directions on a compass are north (N), south (S), east (E) and west (W), and of the meaning of NE, SW, etc. These are examples of **compass bearings**. A **bearing** is a specified direction in relation to a fixed line. The line that is usually taken is due north, the symbol for which is:

  The students will have probably seen this symbol on maps in Geography.
- Explain that bearings are mainly used for navigation purposes at sea and in the air, and in sports such as orienteering. (Fell walkers will probably also use them when walking in mist and fog!)
- The class can copy this into their books: 'A bearing is measured in degrees (°) and the angle is always measured **clockwise** from the **north line**. A bearing is always given using three digits and so is sometimes referred to as a **three-figure bearing**. For example, the bearing for an easterly direction is 090°.' (This is pronounced as 'a bearing of zero nine zero'.)
- Draw the diagram shown on the board, and explain that the three-figure bearing of B from A is 040° and the three-figure bearing of A from B is 220°:

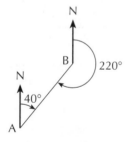

- Work through another example, including the calculation:
  Bearing of B from A = Bearing of A from B + 180°
- Draw the diagram to the right on the board and explain how to find the bearing of Leeds from Manchester and the bearing of Manchester from Leeds: The bearing of Leeds from Manchester is 050° and the bearing of Manchester from Leeds is 230°. The difference between the two bearings is 180°. These are often referred to as 'back bearings'.

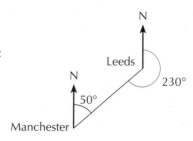

- **The class can now do Exercise 15F from Pupil Book 1.**

Plenary

- Ask individual students to explain the difference between compass bearings and three-figure bearings.
- Ask them to convert from one to the other by giving a few examples.

Key Words
- bearing
- three-figure bearing
- scale drawing
- north line
- clockwise

Homework

1 Write down each of the following compass bearings as three-figure bearings:

a north **b** east **c** north-west **d** south-east

2 Write down the three-figure bearing of B from A for each of the following:

a **b** 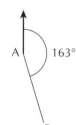 **c** **d**

3 Draw a rough sketch to show each of the bearings below (mark the angle on each sketch):

a From a ship P, the bearing of a harbour Q is 070°.

b From a helicopter S, the bearing of a landing pad T is 100°.

c From a rocket R, the bearing of the Moon M is 225°.

d From an aeroplane Y, the bearing of an airport Z is 310°.

4 The diagram shows the positions of a tanker at sea, a light-house and a harbour:

a Find the bearing of the tanker from the light-house.

b Find the bearing of the tanker from the harbour.

c Find the bearing of the harbour from the light-house.

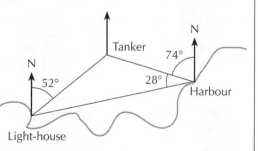

Answers
1 a 000° **b** 090° **c** 315° **d** 135°
2 a 070° **b** 163° **c** 265° **d** 340°
3 Sketches of bearings: **a** 070° **b** 100° **c** 225° **d** 310°
4 a 052° **b** 286° **c** 078°

LESSON 15.8

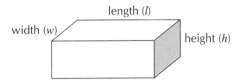

Framework objectives – A cube investigation

Calculate the surface area of cubes and cuboids and shapes made from cuboids.

Oral and mental starter

● On the board, draw a cube similar to the one shown.

length (*l*)

width (*w*)

height (*h*)

● Ask the class to write down the formula for the total surface area of the cuboid. Check their answers. Make sure they use the correct notation for the formula, i.e.

$$A = 2lw + 2lh + 2hw$$

Main lesson activity

● A cube investigation.

● This investigation focuses on the students' ability to represent 3-D shapes on isometric paper and to explain their methods when solving a problem. The students can work in pairs or in groups. Each pair or group will require a collection of cubes and centimetre isometric dotted paper (multi-link cubes are ideal for this investigation).

● The problem is outlined in Pupil Book 1 on page 186 and repeated here.
Two cubes can only be arranged in one way to make a solid shape:
  Copy the diagram onto isometric dotted paper.
  The surface area of the solid is 10 cm².

Three cubes can be arranged in two different ways.
  Copy the diagrams onto isometric dotted paper.
  The surface area of both solids is 14 cm².

or

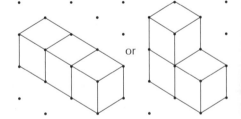

Here is an arrangement of four cubes.

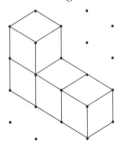

The surface area of the solid is 18 cm².
How many different arrangements can you make using four cubes?
Draw all the different arrangements on isometric dotted paper.
What is the greatest surface area for the different solids you have made?
What is the least surface area for the different solids you have made?

Make a table to show your results and write down anything you notice.
What do you think is the greatest and least surface area of a solid made from five cubes?

There are seven different arrangements:

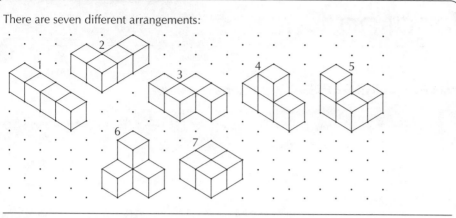

Solid	1	2	3	4	5	6	7
Surface area	18 cm²	18 cm²	18 cm²	18 cm²	18 cm²	18 cm²	16 cm²

Solid 7 has the least surface area and the rest have the same surface area.
The solid with the least surface area has four pairs of faces touching, whereas the other six have three pairs of faces touching.
For all the solids in this investigation, the surface area is an even number of square centimetres.
Two cubes have 12 faces in total, so if one pair of faces are touching, then 10 faces are exposed.
Three cubes have 18 faces in total, so if two pairs of faces are touching, then 14 faces are exposed.
A solid made from four cubes must have three or four pairs of faces touching, so either 16 or 18 faces are exposed.
A solid made from five cubes must have four or five pairs of faces touching, so either 20 or 22 faces are exposed.

SATs Answers

1 a quadrilateral and kite   b (5, 7)
2 b 5.6 cm (± 2 mm)   b 112 m (± 4 m)
3 a

b an example of a net

Plenary

- Towards the end of the lesson, some discussion of the methods the students used to carry out the investigation could take place.

Key Words

- investigate
- cube
- surface area

Handling Data 3

CHAPTER 16

LESSON 16.1

Framework objectives – Frequency tables
Design a data collection sheet or questionnaire to use in a simple survey. Construct frequency tables for discrete data, grouped where appropriate in equal class intervals.

Oral and mental starter

- Write a table on the board or an OHT, as shown below.

Birthday	Tally	Frequency
Jan – Mar		
Apr – Jun		
Jul – Sep		
Oct – Dec		

- Collect data from the students and record it in the tally column. Use a student to do the recording.
- Ask the students to complete the frequency column.
- Now ask a series of brief questions about the data. For example:
  Which period has the most birthdays?
  How many students are present in the class?
  How many students have birthdays in the first half of the year?

Main lesson activity

- Have a selection of different sized books or other objects set out for this activity.
- Tell the class that part of the task is to measure objects to the nearest centimetre. Remind them when to round up and when to round down.
- Draw on the board or on an OHT a table, as shown below.

Height of book (nearest centimetre)	Tally	Frequency
22–24		
25–27		
28–30		
31–33		

- Ask the class to measure, to the nearest centimetre, the height of different books or other objects.
- Tell them to copy the table into their books and record their responses.
- Explain to the class that you want them to measure at least 15 objects and then to complete the frequency table.
- Finally, ask them to write down at least two facts about their table.
- Complete the frequency table.

- **The class can now do Exercise 16A from Pupil Book 1.**

1

Time (minutes)	Number of customers
0–10	13
11–20	7
21–30	7

2

Height (metres)	Number of people
1.4–1.5	6
1.6–1.7	11
1.8–1.9	3

b 1.6–1.7

3

Mass (kilograms)	Number of fish
0 – 2	4
3 – 5	9
6 – 8	1

b 6–8

4

Temperature (°C)	Frequency
8–10	3
11–13	7
14–16	4
17–19	2

b 11–13

Plenary

- Tell the class to copy out another table.

Tally	Frequency
0–10	
11–20	
21–30	
31–40	

- Explain that you are going to call out numbers which they will record using five bar gates.
- Tell the students that when anyone gets ten in one class, she/he has to put up a hand.
- When the hands go up, ask those students to total the frequency column.
- Ask them now for the total frequency and the number in the smallest class.

Key Words

- [ ] **discrete**
- [ ] **data**
- [ ] **sample size**
- [ ] **frequency table**

Homework

1 Complete a frequency table for the following temperatures (°C). Use class intervals of 0–10, 11–20, 21–30, 31–40.

12	17	32	30	10	22	26	8	16	5
14	33	24	19	6	30	25	40	2	18

2 Complete a frequency table for the ages (years) of a group of people. Use class intervals of 20–24, 25–29, 30–34, 35–40.

24	28	25	36	30	37	33	22	27	39
22	29	34	21	31	30	29	21	32	35

3 Complete a frequency table for the marks that students scored in a test. Use class intervals of 0–10, 11–20, 21–30, 31–40.

25	32	10	39	19	9	38
24	32	35	11	21	34	22

Answers

1

Temperature (°C)	Frequency
0–10	5
11–20	6
21–30	6
31–40	3

2

Age (years)	Frequency
20–24	5
25–29	5
30–34	6
35–40	4

3

Marks	Frequency
0–10	2
11–20	2
21–30	4
31–40	6

Framework objectives – The median

Calculate statistics for small sets of discrete data. Find the mode, median and range.

Oral and mental starter

- Use a target board, as shown below.

8	5	2	9	6
4	3	5	6	8

- Ask the class to give you the ten numbers in ascending order.
- Now ask them to give you the numbers in descending order.
- Now show them a three-by-three target board, as shown below.

4	6	2
3	9	5
2	8	4

- Ask the students to give you the nine numbers in ascending order.
- Now ask them to give you the numbers in descending order.
- Ask them to tell you, without repeating all the numbers, which is, for example, the third number when the numbers are in ascending order.
- Repeat this for the fifth number.

Main lesson activity

- Tell the class that the aim of the lesson is to work out the **median** of a set of data.
- Go back to the three-by-three target board and ask them to tell you again the fifth number when the numbers are in ascending order.
- Now ask the class for the fifth number when they are arranged in descending order.
- Prompt the class to point out that it is the same number. Tell them that as it is the middle number, it is called the median.
- Repeat this for different sets of data.
- Now write down ten numbers. You could use the numbers from the target board used earlier:

8	5	2	9	6
4	3	5	6	8

- Ask the students to put these numbers in order, smallest first:
  2   3   4   5   5   6   6   8   8   9
- Establish that there are two middle numbers (5 and 6).
- Explain that the median is in the middle of those two, hence its value is 5.5.

- **The class can now do Exercise 16B from Pupil Book 1.**

1 **a** 5 **b** 24 **c** 11 **d** 106
2 **a** 15.5 **b** 5 **c** 75 **d** 111
3 **a** 20 kg **b** £1.78 **c** 103.5 cm **d** 22 litres
4 **a** For example: 8, 9, *10*, 11, 12
   b For example: 5, 6, 7, *8*, 9, 10, 11
   c For example: 12, 13, *14*, *14*, 15, 16
   d For example: 8, 9, 10, 11, *11*, *13*, 13, 14, 15, 16
5 17 lengths
6 £1.90

Plenary

- Write two numbers on the board. Ask the class to give you the median.
- Now write an extra number on the board and ask the class for the new median.
- Keep adding numbers and repeating.
- At some stage, add an extreme value to the data to show that it does not affect the median value.

- median
- middle value
- data
- set of data

Homework

1 Find the median of each of the following sets of data.

   a 7, 5, 2, 3, 9, 2, 5, 7, 6   **b** 46, 37, 25, 14, 41, 27, 29, 33, 25

   c 6, 1, 10, 15, 11, 15, 7   **d** 100, 95, 73, 67, 34, 121, 164, 241, 503

2 Find the median of each of the following sets of data.

   a 21, 17, 25, 18, 14, 20   **b** 7, 2, 8, 5, 3, 1, 4, 7, 9, 5

   c 204, 153, 88, 157   **d** 28, 33, 49, 56, 51, 104

Answers
 1 **a** 5 **b** 29 **c** 10 **d** 100
 2 **a** 19 **b** 5 **c** 155 **d** 50

Framework objectives – Drawing frequency diagrams

Construct, on paper and using ICT, graphs and diagrams to represent data, including frequency diagrams for grouped discrete data. *(Year 7 objective.)*

Oral and mental starter

- Put on the board the words *frequency, table, collect, tally, diagram* and *data*.
- Ask the class to sort the words into an order that they can explain. For example:
  collect data, tally, frequency table, diagram.
- Now ask the class to make the words into a complete sentence. For example:
  I am going to collect some data together in a tally chart, which I will then set out as a frequency table and use the data to draw a frequency diagram.
- Add other words such as *compare, statistic* and *discrete*.
- This starter can be used to establish a set order of working with statistics, but it can also be used as part of the literacy strategy. A further step would be to ask students to spell some of the words before putting them on the board.

Main lesson activity

- Sketch a bar chart on the board or an OHT. Leave gaps between the bars and label the bars *cats, dogs,* etc.
- Sketch on the board or an OHT, a bar-line graph and label the lines *1, 2, 3,* etc.
- Ask the class what the differences are between the two diagrams. They will probably first point out the difference in width of the bars and lines.
- Now draw a bar chart and label the bars *0–10, 11–20,* etc. Leave gaps between the bars.
- Ask them why there are gaps on all these diagrams. Lead them into talking about **discrete data**.
- Write down a checklist of what is needed to make a good frequency diagram for discrete data:
  - Title
  - Suitable equal class intervals
  - Axes labelled
  - Bars labelled
  - Neat, ruled bars or lines
  - No gaps
- The class can now copy this checklist into their books.

- **The class can now do Exercise 16C from Pupil Book 1.**

Plenary

- Ask some students to list the main features which make a good frequency diagram.
- Rehearse the list that you have already given to them.
- Emphasise the importance of writing clear labels on the axes, using a ruler to construct the bars and ensuring that the spaces between the bars are equal.
- Add to this list if you need to.

Key Words

- bar chart
- bar-line graph
- frequency diagram
- discrete data

1 a

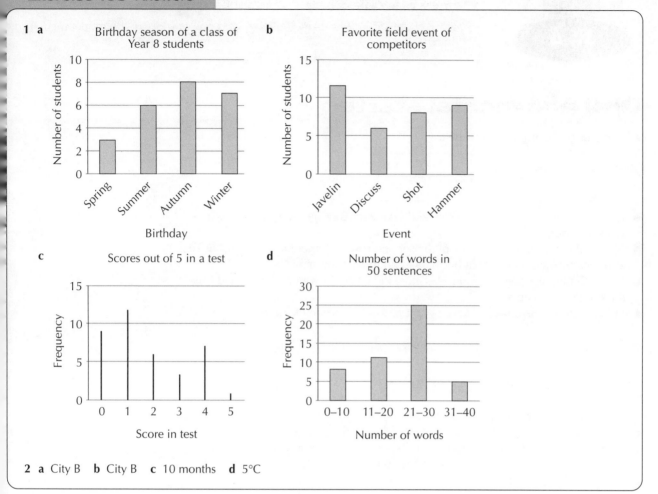

Birthday season of a class of Year 8 students

b Favorite field event of competitors

c Scores out of 5 in a test

d Number of words in 50 sentences

2 a City B **b** City B **c** 10 months **d** 5°C

1 For each frequency table, construct a bar chart.

a Bus journey times.

Time (minutes)	Frequency
0–20	12
21–40	15
41–60	9
61–80	4

b Mean temperatures of 37 European regions

Average temperature (°C)	Frequency
0–5	4
6–10	8
11–15	12
16–20	9
21–25	4

Answers

1 a

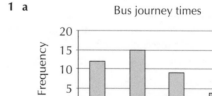

Bus journey times

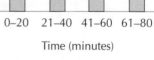

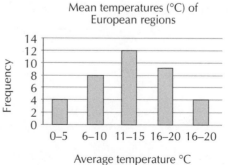

Mean temperatures (°C) of European regions

Framework objectives – Comparing data

Compare two distributions using the range and one or more of the mode, median and mean.

Oral and mental starter

- Use a target board, as shown below.

1	3	5	7	9	11	13
2	4	6	8	10	12	14

- Ask the class to look at the top row and give you its **range**. Ask them how they worked it out.
- Now ask the class for the range of the second row. Ask them to compare the first and second rows. Say: 'What has happened to each number?'
- Establish that, although the numbers have increased by one in the second row, the range is unchanged.
- This starter can be repeated for different second rows: for example, 2, 6, 10, 14, 18, 22, 26.
- Prompt the students to tell you the effect on the range each time.

Main lesson activity

- Write on the board five numbers: for example 3, 6, 7, 5, 9.
- Ask the students to give you the total (30), the mean (6), the range (6).
- Now write on the board five more numbers: for example, 4, 7, 4, 5, 10.
- Again, ask them to give you the total (30), the mean (6), the range (6).
- Point out that although the numbers are different the answers happen to be the same.
- Now introduce the idea of comparing averages and ranges. Draw a table on the board.

	A	B
Mean	5	10
Range	6	3

- Discuss the differences. Use phrases such as 'B is less spread out than A'; 'B's data is generally higher than A's'
- Emphasise that they have to compare the data given in such a question, not just repeat it.

- **The class can now do Exercise 16D from Pupil Book 1.**

1 100°C
2 3.5s
3 15 minutes, 25 minutes, 16 minutes, 8 minutes, 17 minutes
4 **a** 10°C, 11°C, 12.5°C, 13°C   **b** The further South the greater the range
5 **a** Matt did better overall as his mean is higher
  b Matt is also more consistent as his range is lower
6 **a** Lisa appears to do better overall as her median score is higher
  b Kyle's scores are more consistent as his range is smaller
8 Generally, men have bigger feet but more variation in size
  a £7   **b** £6.50

Plenary

Key Words

- Give an example of two golfers whose scores are respectively: 4, 4, 5, 4, 4, 4, 5 and 6.
- Now talk about different students spending considerably different lengths of time on their homework. Give an example.
- Move on to different average times and less consistency.
- Now set the homework!

Key Words
- comparison
- range
- mode
- median
- mean

Homework

1 The table shows the mean and range of a set of golf scores per hole for Emily and Lorna.

	Emily	Lorna
Mean	4.2	6.1
Range	4	3

Compare the mean and range and explain what they tell you.

2 The table shows the median and range of weekly sales of two magazines.

	Teen Mag	Only 13
Median	12 000	14 000
Range	1000	3500

Compare the median and range and explain what they tell you.

3 The table shows the mode and range of goals scored by two hockey teams.

	Rotherfield	Shefham
Mode	3	5
Range	1	4

Compare the mode and range and explain what they tell you.

Answers
1 Emily has a better mean score, so she will win most holes, but Lorna's scores show less variation
2 *Teen Mag* sells fewer per week, but sales of *Only 13* fluctuate far more
3 Shefham generally score more goals, but are less consistent than Rotherfield

Framework objectives – Which average to use?
Recognise when it is appropriate to use range, mean, median and mode.

Oral and mental starter

- Ask the class to give you three numbers with a mode of 5.
- Ask the class to give you three numbers with a median of 6.
- Ask the class to give you three numbers with a mean of 7.
- Ask the class to give you three numbers with a range of 8.
- Ask the class whether they can make the same three numbers work for more than one statement. For example, 5, 5 and 13 have a mode of 5 and a range of 8.
- Ask the class to give you three numbers and tell you two facts about the numbers. For example, 3, 5 and 10 have a median of 5 and a range of 7.

Main lesson activity

- Write on the board or an OHT a set of data. For example, 3, 3, 3, 3, 3, 3, 3, 3, 3, 100.
- Ask the class to tell you the mode. Ask them to explain how they know.
- Now ask for the median. Again, ask them to explain how they know.
- Ask them whether the mean will also be 3. Prompt them to explain that it must be bigger because of the 100, which affects the mean.
- Discuss the disadvantages of using the mean in this case. Explain that the 100 is sometimes called a rogue or **extreme value**.
- Explain that this lesson will look at all types of average and why sometimes one type is better than another.
- Recap the meaning of mode, median, mean and range.
- Now look at the table of advantages and disadvantages in Pupil Book 1, page 198.
- Talk through the examples given in the fourth column.
- Now ask the students to write down their own sets of numbers which satisfy each statement. For example, write down a set of numbers where the mean would be a suitable average and a set of numbers where the mean would not be a suitable average.
- They could work in small groups for this activity.
- Explain that the guidelines are not set in stone and that some data requires caution when concluding whether an average is suitable or not.

- **The class can now do Exercise 16E from Pupil Book 1.**

1 a Mean is suitable as the data is evenly distributed
  b Mode is suitable as it is a central value
  c Median is suitable as it is a central value
  d Mode may not be suitable as it is an extreme value
  e Median may not be suitable as it is an extreme value
  f Mean may not be suitable as it is affected by an extreme value
2 a Mode = 10
  b Median is a central value but the mode is at one end of the data.
3 a Could be unsuitable as one extreme value distorts result
  b Suitable as data is evenly spread.
  c Could be unsuitable as one extreme value distorts result
  d Suitable as data is evenly spread
  e Suitable as there is plenty of data at both extremes
  f Suitable as data is evenly spread

Plenary

- Write down a small set of data on the board. For example, 0, 1, 3, 3, 3, 50.
- Ask the class to write down which average (mode, median or mean) they would not use.
- Now ask them to reveal their answers and give a reason for rejecting the mean.
- Repeat for different data. For example, 6, 6, 6, 6, 8, 9, 10.
- Remind the class of the main advantages and disadvantages of using each average.

Key Words

- mode
- mean
- median
- extreme value
- appropriate data
- central value

Homework

1 Look at each set of data and the average which has been calculated. Say whether you think it is a suitable average to use.

  a 1, 2, 4, 8, 10, 11   Mean = 6   b 2, 2, 2, 2, 4, 6, 8   Mode = 2

  c 2, 4, 6, 8, 10, 11, 11 Median = 8   d 2, 2, 2, 3, 5, 6, 6   Mode = 2

  e 1, 2, 4, 6, 8, 8, 8   Median = 6   f 1, 28, 29, 31, 34, 39   Mean = 27

2 Look at each set of data. Decide whether the range is suitable or not. Explain your answer.

  a 2, 3, 6, 8, 9, 10   b 1, 1, 1, 1, 20   c 2, 2, 4, 6, 8

  d 1, 2, 5, 7, 8, 9   e 1, 2, 2, 2, 8, 9, 9, 20

Answers
  1 a Mean is suitable as the data is evenly distributed
    b Mode may not suitable as it is an extreme value
    c Median is suitable as it is a central value
    d Mode may not be suitable as it is an extreme value
    e Median may be suitable although it is numerically closer to one end than the other
    f Mean may not be suitable as it is affected by an extreme value
  2 a Suitable as data is evenly spread
    b Could be unsuitable as one extreme value distorts result
    c Suitable as data is evenly spread
    d Suitable as data is evenly spread
    e Could be unsuitable as one extreme value distorts result

LESSON 16.6

Framework objectives – Experimental and theoretical probability

Communicate orally and on paper the results of a statistical enquiry and the methods used, using ICT as appropriate. Justify the choice of what is presented.

Compare experimental and theoretical probabilities in different contexts.

Oral and mental starter

- Place 20 small pieces of card of different colours, say 10 red and 10 blue, in a bag.
- Ask a student to pick out a piece of card without looking at the rest of the cards. Show it to the class. Ask the class what this tells them about the pieces of card in the bag. Replace it and shuffle the pieces up. Repeat several times.
- Tell the class that there are 20 pieces of card in the bag coloured red or blue. Ask a student to predict how many there are of each.
- You may need to repeat this several times.
- Reveal the number by emptying the bag.
- Ask the class how many times they would expect to get red if they picked out and replaced ten times.
- Tell them that the theoretical probability is $\frac{1}{2}$.

Main lesson activity

- Continuing from the starter, have a bag with, for example, 5 red and 15 blue pieces of card.
- Ask a student to pick out a card and replace it ten times.
- Record the result on the board.
- Repeat a further ten times and record the result of the first 20 colours.
- Keep repeating and recording until sufficient trials have been carried out (for example, 40 trials) to enable the students to estimate accurately the number of red cards to blue cards. Remind them that there are 20 cards in the bag altogether.
- Emphasise that if you had carried out the test more times, you would expect the results for the experimental and theoretical probabilities to be closer together, which may or may not happen.
- Finish off this part by saying that they will have to devise experiments of their own to compare the probabilities.

- **The class can now do Exercise 16F from Pupil Book 1.**

All the questions in this exercise involve carrying out experiments and comparing answers with those given for the theoretical probabilities. The answers will vary according to the results obtained.

SATs Answers

1 a Spinner A, as it is 1 out of 5 rather than 1 out of 6 for spinner B
  b Does not matter, angles at the centre are the same
  c Spaces will be filled with 3, 3, 4, 4, 4, in any order
2 a 6 **b** 1 and 5
  c for example: 1 and 3 and 5 (3 numbers total = 9, range = 4)
3 a Sue; more trials **b** $\frac{171}{300}$

Plenary

Key Words

- Put 19 red cards and 1 blue card in a bag.
- Ask a pupil to keep picking a card out and replacing it.
- Tell the class that there are 20 cards in the bag and ask them to write down how many reds they think are in the bag. Tell them that they can change their answer after every pick.
- If the blue does is not picked for a while they may put 20 as their answer.
- You can choose when to reveal the correct answer.

Key Words
- biased
- event
- experimental probability
- theoretical probability

Homework

1 A dice is rolled 60 times. It lands on 6 fifteen times. Do you think that the dice is fair? Explain your answer.

2 A coin is tossed 30 times. It lands on Tails 14 times. Do you think it is fair? Explain your answer.

3 Think of a probability experiment that you can carry out. Record your results and comment on whether the results are what you expected.

Answers
  1 Possibly not, as you would expect it to land on 6 only ten times
  2 It probably is fair, as you would expect it to land on Tails 15 times and 14 is very close
  3 As this question involves an experiment, the answers will vary

Published by HarperCollins*Publishers* Limited
77–85 Fulham Palace Road
Hammersmith
London
W6 8JB

www.**Collins**Education.com
Online support for schools and colleges

10 9 8 7 6 5 4 3 2 1

ISBN 0 00 713864 4

Keith Gordon, Kevin Evans, Trevor Senior and Brian Speed assert their moral rights to be identified as the authors of this work.

British Library Cataloguing in Publication Data
A Catalogue record for this publication is available from the British Library

Edited by John Day
Typesetting and design by Derek Lee
Project Management by Sam Holmes
Covers by Tim Byrne
Illustrations by Derek Lee
Additional proofreading by Graham Walker
CD mastering by Alan Trewartha
Production by Emma Johnson
Printed and bound by Martins the Printers, Berwick upon Tweed

The publishers would like to thank the many teachers and advisers whose feedback helped to shape *Maths Frameworking*.

You might also like to visit:
www.**fire**and**water**.com
The book lover's website